MW00861299

Special people.

Marge Knuth

The
PROFESSIONAL
Activity
Director

Disclaimer

MOST IDEAS SHARED in this book have been personally tried by the author and found successful. They are not, however, meant to be a foolproof plan. This book is intended to be a helpful tool only. The ideas are freely submitted for your use, and hopefully, for your success though the author can take no responsibility for any failure or harm resulting from the use of the ideas or any material presented in this book.

The
PROFESSIONAL
Activity
Director

by Marge Knoth

Valley Press
Lafayette, Indiana

Copyright © 1989, 1994 by Marge Knoth
Second printing: May 1991,
Third printing: December 1994

ALL RIGHTS RESERVED

No part of this book may be reproduced
in any form or by any electronic means without
written permission from the author,
with the exception that a reviewer may quote a
brief passage for a review.

ISBN Number   0-927935-07-4

Foreword

by Richard E. Linson, Sr.

Whether you are a newly certified activity director or a long-time professional, whether you are a director of nurses or a volunteer, *The Professional Activity Director* will add depth and dimension to your facility's activity program.

I first had the pleasure of meeting the author, Marge Knoth, in 1979 when she applied for the position of activity director at my facility. In those days, certification for activity directors was not a prerequisite, and resource materials were limited. Our program was in the pits. It was obvious that Mrs. Knoth was enthusiastic and the type of individual our program needed. Having no previous experience in activities and no one to train her, Marge put together an activity program that was the envy of my fellow administrators. She developed programs that not only brought the community into the facility, but also allowed our residents to reach out and remain active individuals who continued to serve and to be involved in their community. I would be amazed at times with the ideas--which seemed never ending--that Marge would come to me with, and I would be even more amazed when she carried them out. For example: hatching baby chickens and ducks, making baby gowns and giving them to the local hospitals to send home with the newborns having just arrived during the Christmas season, making sock dolls to send to needy children overseas, and having a Christmas party for needy children--and getting local service clubs to sponsor it. One of her most ambitious ventures was to organize a nursing home olympics that included participation from most all the facilities in our district, an annual event that continues with senior citizens, in a form, yet today.

A top-notch activity program, in addition to having an enthusiastic and imaginative director, must have the support of the facility administrator and staff, must generate interest for residents, and must include the residents' families and the community. The administrator also must be willing to support the program financially.

If you, the reader, have a struggling activity program and will incorporate the ideas of this book into your program, you can expect to see much improvement. If you already have a successful program, you can use the ideas and methods presented in this book as a valuable enhancement. The beginning activities professional can build a firm foundation from the material in this book. To Marge Knoth, may God bless you and your book.

Richard E. Linson, Sr.
Administrator/Owner
Comfort Retirement & Nursing Home
Lafayette, Indiana 47901

Editor's Note and Special Credits

A PERSONAL NOTE to all male activity directors and to all female administrators for the choice of pronouns used in this book: After writing the first chapter, it became apparent that using both pronouns *he/she* would hamper the natural flow of words, so the author simply chose *she* when referring to activity directors, and to give equal time, *he* for administrators.

THE NAMES OF THE RESIDENTS have been changed with the exception of Opel and Bertha Linson and Vivian Eaton who appear in chapter five. *ABC* is a fictitious name for the facility described.

PHOTO CREDITS: Cover photo by Fred Butz, owner of *Camera Craftsman* in Lafayette, Indiana. Appearing in it are resident, Bertha Linson and author, Marge Knoth. Other photos are courtesy of the *Journal and Courier* in Lafayette, Indiana.

COVER AND LAYOUT DESIGN: Dallas Pasco, Lawrence, Kansas

A SPECIAL THANKS to Lisa Talbert who helped much in editing the manuscript.

SOME OF THE WORD GAMES in chapter eleven are not original and the author takes no credit for them. Unfortunately, as they as they have been around for many years, she was unable to locate their author.

To Rick...

...my best friend, my constant encourager, my high school sweetheart and my devoted husband of 32 years: A very special thanks for the untold hours at the computer doing the technical part of this manuscript as well as for handling all the financial matters and numerous other aspects involved in the publication of this book. Without you, I might never have made it.

Table of Contents

Foreword: Richard E. Linson, Sr.

Extras For You

CHAPTER 1

The Fun and Games Lady:
What Does She *Really* Do?

Your job is such that nobody knows exactly what you do yet everyone is aware when you're not there. In a long-term care facility, administrative, nursing, and dietary roles are well defined. Staff members know exactly what *they* do, but the role of the activity director to others is often vague. You are greatly loved by the families of residents, and you are respected by the community at large--if you have done your job of reaching out to them. Yet, like a prophet not being accepted in his home town, too often are you, the activity director in your own facility.

Co-workers notice that you wear pretty clothes while they, working in other departments, must wear uniforms. You sit in your office many hours rather than entertaining residents, they deduce, and you have volunteers to do your work for you. It's an easy job they think--planning parties, welcoming interesting guests, decorating the facility and overseeing activities. Sometimes even your administrator doesn't know what you *really* do with your time.

It's unfortunate that many administrators do not recognize the activity director's role is every bit as professional as that of the director of nurses and the dietitian. Sometimes, unknowingly though, that may be the fault of you, the activity director. You may not have made him aware of your value to him and to the facility, and you may not have alerted him to the many hats you really wear. If your administrator is unaware of your many responsibilities as activity director, it's no wonder other staff members don't understand them either.

In many facilities you are in it alone. The activity department is a department of one person-- *YOU*--and whatever gets done, or doesn't get done, rests solely on your shoulders. Just putting on an activity--planning it, transporting residents to and from it, carrying it out and cleaning up after it--is a real challenge.

Your position as activity director requires seemingly unlimited charting, record keeping and other paper work. You must be professional enough to deal with influential people and to honor speaking engagements when asked. You must be able to offer a diversified activity program which meets the needs of not only the alert resident, but the senile, the confused, the Alzheimer's victim, the stroke patient, the depressed, the mentally retarded and the developmentally disabled. Yet you must not be too proud to push a broom or to wipe up a puddle.

You find yourself taking continuing education courses, managing a volunteer program, writing a newsletter, dealing with the media, enticing the community into your facility and acting as a liaison between residents and other staff members. You act as a fund raiser, bookkeeper, correspondent, postman and shopper. You are a public relations person, a bus driver, a writer, an animal keeper, a greenhouse tender, a seamstress, a teacher, a tear-wiper and an errand girl to name just a few.

You, as activity director, like a mother in a home, set the mood and personality of your facility. Your job is such that it overlaps every other department so you must be able to get along with co-workers. If you don't, there will be little cooperation, and a negative spirit will filter throughout the facility leaving both staff and residents frustrated and unhappy.

Not everyone can fill the role of activity director. It takes a sensitive, yet firm individual. It requires unlimited energy, physical strength and a soft heart. The activity director must be cooperative, unselfish, organized and willing to listen.

The real challenge of being an activity director comes at the end of a busy day when you, the tired activity director, are cleaning up the final mess of the day and preparing to go home. A resident approaches and asks you a familiar question: "What are we going to do now?"

If you can pull back your shoulders and keep your smile, you've got what it takes to be an activity director.

CHAPTER 2

Is Too Much Being Expected of Activity Directors?

The burnout rate for activity directors is high. The average length of time, it has been estimated, for one to work is eighteen months. Many activity directors are frustrated. Too much is being expected of them. Some are required to act as baby-sitters when the nursing staff becomes weary of caring for difficult residents. Some have limited budgets, and a few are even expected to earn whatever expenses their department requires to operate. Others confess that they are not taken seriously nor given the respect due a department head. And almost unanimously, activity directors claim they are underpaid.

Under circumstances like these, it is no wonder the activity director becomes frustrated and faces burnout. But don't despair just yet! Perhaps you can turn at least some of these situations around and make your job not only more workable, but challenging and stimulating as well.

Let your light shine

Let's begin with the problem of not being taken seriously. Your job is an important one and you, before anyone else, must be convinced of it. *You are a professional,* and when you realize it and convince your administrator and your director of nurses of it, things will begin to change for the better.

Just where do you begin? Let's examine some of the ways in which you can promote yourself and your department to the status where it should be--a status where you can have the respect, though not always the friendship, of others who work in your facility.

The professional look

First, take a good look at yourself. How are you dressed today--jeans? slacks? denim shirt? Though it should not be, people *do* judge you by the clothes you wear. Dressing casually may cause you to be treated less seriously than if you were to dress in a more professional manner. It's easy to argue that activity directors get involved in many things that prevent them from wearing good clothes. Never mind! Jackets come off and aprons go on over nice clothes. Without argument, jeans are more comfortable than skirts, but if you want to earn the respect you deserve, dress professionally. This may mean different things in different areas of the country. Only *you* can decide what's right in your area. Generally, dresses look especially nice and are fairly comfortable. They take little coordinating. A jacket over a dress adds a touch of class. Jackets or blazers over skirts or dressy slacks look nice, too.

For male activity directors, jackets may not be the most comfortable, but how many truly professional men in white collar jobs do you know who do not wear them? No need to struggle with white shirts alone; today's shirts come in handsome, non-traditional colors--pink, turquoise, cinnamon and peach. Whatever your sex, if you dress the part, you'll find yourself being treated by families, staff and residents in a more professional manner.

Buy the best quality clothes you can afford. Well-made garments hang nicer on you than less-expensive ones. It's better to have a few *good* mix-and-match jackets and skirts than a closet *full* of cheaply-made ones. Since good clothes are expensive, affording them may take some creative shopping. Watch for sales. Check out outlet stores and wholesale clubs. And don't overlook resale shops and garage sales. Since women change sizes frequently, you might find some nice brand-name outfits there. You'll feel more confident in better-made clothing.

One way to plan a workable wardrobe is to stick to basic colors-- black, navy, grey, beige--for skirts, slacks and jackets. These can be easily be mixed and matched. By sticking to basic, compatible colors, the combinations are endless. To these, add a half-dozen nice blouses, a couple sweaters, and some attractive accessories.

Unfortunately, our physical size often determines the style of clothing we should wear. Few of us are the perfect shape, so we adapt our clothing to play down our less attractive areas.

For instance, short women do better wearing a single color, an unbroken line, so to speak, rather than one color skirt and a contrasting jacket. This combination would make a short woman appear even shorter. Wearing pastels can cause a short woman to be mistaken for a juvenile. Also, try to avoid too much shoulder padding, large prints and exaggerated details. Tall women are more fortunate. They can wear most anything--just so jacket, sleeves and hemline are long enough.

Recently on a plane, I met a gorgeous high-fashion model. When she learned I was speaking on professional dress, she volunteered: "Tell the larger women to forget baggy clothes. Accentuate what they have. Wear belts--just not too tight ones." Larger women look good in tailored suits, v-necks, and high boots which disappear under the hemline (though boots probably wouldn't be practical for work). Fullness should be at the front of her skirts. Larger women also look good in straight-leg pants.

To further help you achieve a professional image, female activity directors should wear nylons and comfortable dress shoes. The fashion model also recommended you avoid wearing flats to work; instead choose a shoe with a small (even an inch) heel. She says these actually improve your posture. It goes without saying that shoes should be shined regularly and be free of run-down heels. To delay that run-down look, have little rubber caps attached to the heels of your new shoes. This can usually be done right at the shoe store. Or you can buy the rubber caps at any shoe department and staple them on yourself. They cost just a dollar or two and prolong the life of your shoes considerably. A nice leather purse is a good investment. Though it costs more initially, it will far outlast less-expensive ones and will greatly enhance your overall appearance. A woman's purse and her shoes tell a lot about her taste.

Opt for colorful jewelry that's not gaudy. Don't worry if you wear glasses; they add to a woman's professional image. Scarves add a touch of class to an outfit, if they are not so big and cumbersome that they get in your way. Experts say women should tone down make-up in the workplace--unless they are over 45, and then use a little more.

The wrong hairstyle, like improper clothing, can quickly rob you of a professional appearance. Find a hairstyle that's flattering to you. You want to give an up-to-date, chic image that says to the world "I am a professional," and "I can handle whatever comes my way."

Things in your facility may not change immediately with your appearance update, but as you continue to look the part, you will begin to feel like the professional you really are. Others, then, will begin to think of you that way too.

The professional manner

Besides your professional appearance, a professional manner is vital. Politeness and respect to others will return to you in kind. An activity director cannot afford the luxury of taking part in the gossip that so often freely flows among staff. One careless word can bring a whole department down on you, and you can't afford that since your department, in one way or another, overlaps every other department. It's important to keep good communications open. So difficult as it is, resist the temptation to spread anything that could be interpreted wrongly.

Also, be kind even though that kindness may not be returned. Share what's happening in your department with other staff, especially aides who sometimes feel no one tells them anything. Introduce them to new volunteers. Be alert for important happenings in their lives--marriages, births, deaths. Acknowledge these events either in conversation or by writing an encouraging note.Establish good working relationships with department heads.

Where does all your time go?

Next, make a detailed list of every duty for which you are responsible. We mentioned some of these in the last chapter. Your list might include:

- calendar planning
- progress notes
- bedside activities
- volunteer coordinating
- editing a newsletter
- continuing education
- community outreaches
- bulletin boards
- district/state meetings
- shopping for supplies
- delivering mail
- taking pictures
- care plans
- group activities
- outings with residents
- getting press coverage
- holding district and state offices
- decorating the facility
- transporting residents to activities
- plant care
- ordering movies
- public relations

You could probably add many more. When your list is as complete as possible, make a few copies. Keep one as a job description and file the rest until needed.

Do you need to visit your administrator?

If you have a wonderful administrator who regularly supports you and your department, thank the Good Lord. Unfortunately, many are not so wonderful. If your employer is one who expects more activities than you can comfortably handle or is expecting too much of you in other areas, maybe it's time for a heart-to-heart talk. Make an appointment, if necessary, and pay him a visit. Since many duties performed by the activity director are small in nature, her administrator may unintentionally write them off as unimportant. Consequently, he may not be aware of how they all add up to rob you of valuable time.

Take a copy of the job description you just prepared to the administrator's office with you. Administrators think in terms of dollars. Speak his language. Tell him of the high rate of burnout for activity directors. Remind him that training a new one is expensive. Don't cry on his shoulder and complain that you are overworked. Appeal to his reason. Hand him a copy of your job description and go over your duties with him. Once he's aware of just how you spend your time, ask him how he would reschedule it. You might say something like: "Now that you are more aware of the many duties for which I am responsible, do you understand why it's next to impossible to hold five or six activities each day? May I suggest....."; then present him with a more workable solution-- perhaps three daily activities. Explain that residents tire when there is too much entertainment. You might suggest one activity in the morning that could be handled by a volunteer followed by a pre-lunch activity which you lead. This might be exercise or reading a devotional followed by a word game. Finally, suggest that the main activity of the day be in early afternoon before residents tire.

Suggest the evening activity be handled by a department other than activities. For instance, an aide could put on a video and rewind it when over. Dietary staff could serve, before they leave in the evening, wine and cheese or cookies and coffee.

Share with him how the *baby-sitter* problem affects your department. Explain how the nursing department who are often frustrated and at their wits end with difficult residents, find themselves in need of relief. The activity department appears a likely spot to place them. Tell him that you don't mind providing these residents with adequate activities, but that sometimes you are busy with other duties or are in the midst of an activity which is not suitable for such a resident. Encourage him to understand the situation and to back you up when the situation arises. Don't let your emotions get the best of you during this visit, but maintain a professional attitude. Do not be aggressive, but *do* be assertive in the requests you are seeking.

If your visit doesn't change anything

Should your visit not change anything and he still demands more activities than you can handle, don't give up yet. There's a way for you to get your paperwork and other duties completed without being harried and totally worn out. Schedule the required number of activities, but make them activities where your presence is not absolutely required. Coffee group is a good one. Don't worry yourself about rounding up residents. Just leave it open. Announce it, welcome residents who come, provide coffee, and then leave them to visit with one another. List *reading group* on your calendar and have an alert resident read the newspaper or a large-print book to the group. Or simply put *newspaper reading* on your calendar as an activity and make sure a newspaper is available. *Plant watering* and *discussion groups* are also acceptable activities as is *tape listening.* Gather residents around and put on tapes of old-time radio shows like *Jack Benny, Amos and Andy* or *George and*

Gracie. Serving popcorn or donuts provides residents with a good incentive to come.

Actually handling the baby-sitter problem

As for the *baby-sitter* problem, you've already asked your administrator to back you up in the matter. Hopefully he will but there's always the chance he won't. Either way, develop a good working relationship with your director of nurses. You may get along well with her which is a great help in this matter but perhaps you don't. Maybe you do not even like each other. If that's the case, you can still develop a positive working relationship. It's very important that she understand your role as activity director. You are not *under* her, nor are you *over* her. You should not compete with her or challenge her, nor should you allow yourself to be threatened by her position. You are equals. She is a department head, and you are a department head. When this becomes clear, things will start to look up. Do not allow yourself to be intimidated by her, but seek to give when necessary so she will do the same for you. Never put her nursing staff down because this could easily put her on the defensive causing greater friction between you. You might give her a copy of your job description so she will be familiar with the many duties that you actually handle. Explain the *baby-sitter* problem to her and ask if she has any suggestions. Put in this manner, chances are she will begin to work *with* you and not *against* you. If after this you still do not get cooperation and disruptive or troublesome residents are brought in for an inappropriate activity or you are asked to find something for someone to do when you are busy with other things, be firm. Simply say, "I'm sorry; I wish I could help you out, but at the moment I have other obligations." Should this not work, take the matter up with your administrator again. If he values you, he will understand and see to it that the situation is taken care of.

Managing on a shoestring

Activity directors often do not receive ample money to run their department. Some don't receive any at all and are expected to earn whatever it takes. This is an unfortunate situation and many activity directors (myself included) would refuse to work for such a facility. It's likely your administrator will not change much on the money he allots to the activity department. If that's the case, an activity director can still run her department well even on a small amount. Activity directors have carried out successful programs on a dollar a month per patient or less. On a shallow budget like this, though, one cannot do many expensive crafts. An activity director must then bring in free entertainment such as musicians, dancers or community people who can demonstrate various skills. These might include painting, woodworking or cake decorating. You can get on a free-loan movie circuit where you pay only the return postage. Also, many people who travel extensively love to show off slides of their trips. Invite them to come and provide residents with an armchair vacation.

You can also hold reminiscent groups and get residents talking about the good old days. You can offer popcorn parties and bingo. Prizes can be obtained by advertising for them in local church bulletins and in your own newsletter. You can invite other facilities to join yours for basketball games (see page 162) or for discussion groups. There are numerous ways to run a quality program on a tight budget. We'll expound more on these later.

Why can't you be paid what you're worth?

As far as being underpaid, an activity director can earn regular raises. Notice the word *earn*. Administrators, as we said before, think in dollars. If you begin to think the same way, you're on your way to higher wages. It's up to you as activity director to present your facility's name in a positive light before the public. This, in turn, helps keep beds full. Do this by providing exciting activities and by learning how to write enticing press releases (see chapter five) that will tempt the media to come and see what's going on.

Plan things that are a little different from what the general public might expect as activities for a long-term care facility. Reach out to the community and find ways your residents can give of themselves. This brings media coverage which is free publicity. Free publicity should make your administrator more aware of your value to him. Then you are in a better position to bargain for higher wages. Don't be afraid to ask for the same salary nurses receive. After all, you are a department head and most of the nurses are not.

Summary

If you have struggled with some of these problems common to activity directors, know that you are not alone. We are all in it together. Just continue to remind yourself that you are a professional and don't quit doing it until you believe it with all your heart. No, don't quit until you have residents, staff, families and all who come into your facility believing it as well.

YOU are a professional!

CHAPTER 3

Getting Organized

When staff or residents need anything--needle and thread, wrapping paper, greeting cards--they usually look for you, the activity director. But the question is: "Can you find it at a moment's notice?" There's so much to do and so little time. Generally, the last thing you have time for is cleaning out files, drawers, cupboards and basically getting organized. Yet that is one definite step you can take toward making your department more efficient and your job easier.

A place for you

Too often the activity director is hired and finds her desk shoved in the corner of a room with supplies falling out all around her. This should not be. You need an office of your own, or at least a designated area separated from the clutter of supplies, unfinished activity projects and the constant interruption of residents. You should not fear voicing your needs to your administrator. If an office is out of the question, ask for attractive dividers to separate your desk area from the clutter. There are few facilities where a room or an area cannot be found to provide the A.D. a place of her own.

Whether your working space is a nice office or just a corner somewhere, it's important that you make it personally yours. Surround yourself with things you like. It might be a plant, photos of your children or some favorite art work. Display your diploma and/or certificates. These help further your image of professionalism in the eyes of those who visit your office. No doubt, there won't be room for a lot, so choose carefully the things that make *you* feel good.

Organizing the activity cabinet

Since so many items come through the activity department, it is imperative that you have ample storage space and a workable retrieval system. A metal storage cabinet with shelves is great. This cabinet, if it has doors to shut out the clutter, can be effectively stored in your office or work area. Shoe boxes can be an activity director's best friend. Shelves of the storage cabinet can be lined with them, setting side by side. Filled with regularly needed supplies, their contents can be labeled in black marker on the end of each box. There might be one box marked sewing supplies, another camera supplies, another playing cards and yet another tapes. Other boxes might be labeled: craft supplies, paints, food supplies and funeral ribbons (all neatly rolled up and paper-clipped, of course). Typing or computer paper boxes are ideal for holding quilt blocks and bingo prizes. These are stored on deeper shelves. Construction paper can be stacked according to color and laid neatly on a shallow shelf. This cupboard is for frequently used items only. In addition to this cupboard, activity directors need an *overflow* area for storing larger items such as fabric, popcorn poppers, seasonal decorations and ice cream freezers. This area might be a large closet somewhere, or a basement storage room.

These items, too, can be packed in boxes--larger, clearly-labeled ones--which are stored on shelves for easy retrieval.

Your filing system

Activity directors need a good supply of file folders and a file drawer or cabinet in which to keep them. Create a file for anything you might need to locate quickly: exercises, gardening information, ideas, incoming-letters, outgoing-letters, job description, movie information and forms. A bookshelf in your office is useful for storing reference books. Loose-leaf binders neatly organize resident council notes, volunteer information and word games. You can color-code them for easy locating.

Activity directors always need art work to enhance newsletters, party invitations and other mailings. Why not try clip-art? Clip-art is usually copyright-free black and white line drawings which can be obtained from various sources. Most companies produce a variety of books--holiday, sports, advertising cuts, children, business, health care, romantic cuts, old-days, transportation and more. Libraries carry these books, or even better, purchase your own. One company is *Dover.* Their prices are very affordable (see page 161).

Once you have the clip-art, how do you store it? Simple! Use clear plastic pocket pages that are punched to fit into a 3-ring binder, or a plastic lift-up page photo album. In these, store your copied clip-art according to holidays, beginning in January. Store miscellaneous clip-art in the latter pages of the folder. Keep this volume on your bookshelf for quick retrieval.

Activity contacts

Use three-by-five cards to keep track of individuals and groups who entertain or volunteer. Each card contains the individual or group name, a contact person, address and phone number. In addition, record the date they perform and any special comments such as promptness in arriving and residents' reaction. Keeping up-to-date records in this file simplifies calendar planning each month.

Other helps

A *Rolodex* retains important phone numbers at your fingertips. Whenever you look up a phone number in the phone book, highlight it in yellow. Even though you think you'll never need it again, chances are, sooner or later, you will. Highlighting simplifies the search. Also, to save valuable time each morning, clean your desk off before going home each afternoon. While your mind is racing frantically dwelling on work yet to be done, transfer those responsibilities to paper. When you come in the next morning, you'll know exactly where you left off and can get started quickly.

Decorations

Storing and quickly retrieving flat wall paste-up decorations is not always easy. Here's a solution. Every fall, card stores and/or party-good stores receive from distributors numerous sample calendars. They come packaged in a large file-type box complete with oversized folders. The box is seven-inches deep, eighteen-inches long, and fifteen-inches tall. The lid lifts up somewhat like the small boxes laundry soap comes in. The stores are usually willing to give you the box, the files, and dozens of sample calendars which provide nice pictures. Short of finding this type of box, look for another box in approximately the same dimensions. Make your own file folders by using two sheets of large-size construction paper taped together. On the top corner of each of these folders, tape a three-by-five card for the tab. This storage method keeps flat paste-up decorations neat. The box remains in your overflow area.

Christmas Decorations

(see chapter twelve, *Surviving December*)

Newsletters

Past newsletters can be retrieved easily if you store them in a typing paper box with the latest issue on top. Make a cross-reference as to what's in each issue and store one copy in your files and another with your newsletters. Then, should someone want information from a particular article, you'll have it at your finger-tips.

Just for you

You will probably want to keep a shoe box in your cupboard marked "personal." In it, keep emergency items: safety pins, stamps, loose change, breath mints, a pair of hose and hair spray to stop an unwanted run. Add any other personal items you might need.

Keeping things neat

At least twice a year--maybe January and July--a thorough cleaning and relentless pitching of unneeded items is usually necessary. You may even have to schedule *cleaning day* on your calendar. This cleaning day provides and opportunity to make new friends among the staff. Put all the give-aways in the break room for them to sort through and take as desired. Regularly, when you find yourself with a few minutes, straighten a shelf or two of your activity cupboard, or your bookshelf. This keeps things constantly in order.

Summary

As activity director, you give so much of yourself for everyone else; why not take a little time now for you? Organize to make your life a whole lot easier. After all, you deserve it!

CHAPTER 4

Planning the Activity Calendar

It's the end of the month and there you sit--staring at a blank calendar. Another month of activities are screaming to be planned. You've been so busy--all those new residents to chart on, the phone's been ringing off the hook, the boss wants a big community event planned--and nursing thinks you have to baby-sit with all the disruptive residents!

You want to put your head down and cry. Well, take heart! We're going to show you a method to plan your whole year before it even begins. No longer will you find yourself staring at a blank calendar each month. By investing a couple hours sometime near the end of the year, you can greatly simplify calendar planning for the rest of the year. If you'd like to give it a try, you'll first need a year-at-a-glance calendar. This calendar shows all twelve months on a single sheet. It usually measures about twenty-four by thirty-six inches, and comes on plain or laminated paper. It can be purchased at an office supply store and ranges in price from eight to twenty dollars. You will also need an ordinary twelve-month planning calendar.

Creating a master sheet

First, grab a sheet of typing paper, turn it sideways, and rule off seven columns (each about one-and-a-half inches wide) to make a master list (see page 167). Label columns:

- daily
- weekly
- monthly
- yearly
- occasionally
- seasonally
- new ideas

Now, under the last five column heads, measure down three-and-a-half inches. Draw a line horizontally through these five columns. This basically cuts the columns in half making them shorter than the first two columns. In doing this, you've created five additional columns. Label these lower columns:

- community involvement,
- projects
- fill ins
- outings
- cooking

This completes your master sheet.

List your holidays

Let's begin with the *seasonally* column. Write on this master sheet, under *seasonally,* all the holidays you want to celebrate:

- New Year's Day
- Valentine's Day
- Presidents' Day
- Ground Hog's Day
- Columbus Day
- St. Patrick's Day
- Easter Sunday
- Memorial Day
- Mother's Day
- Labor Day
- Grandparent's Day
- Election Day
- Thanksgiving Day
- Hanukkah
- Christmas

Yearly

Next, under the heading *yearly*, write annual events:
- pet show
- Oktoberfest
- hatching chicks
- fishing trip
- trip to the park
- nursing home olympics

Occasionally

Our next category is *occasionally*. These events may take place two, three or more times a year. Under this heading list:
- baby loving days
- square dancers
- bands
- barber shop quartet

Monthly

Now we turn to the *monthly* column. This becomes a little easier because we are more familiar with our regular events. Here list:
- resident council
- birthday party
- school class visit
- kitchen band
- cooking project
- outing

Weekly

On the *weekly* column on your master sheet, fill in your regularly scheduled activities. These might include:
- movies
- Bible study
- ceramics
- bingo
- church
- reminiscence group

Daily

Also, list all your *daily* activities on your master sheet:
- coffee group
- devotional
- newspaper reading
- exercises
- word games
- current events

New ideas

Under this heading, list any activities you might like to try. You are not committed to actually doing these activities. By putting them on your master sheet, though, you will always have a ready supply of ideas when you want to plan something different. Be sure to keep this column current. You might want to try:

- doll show
- making a comforter
- celebrity day
- county fair
- basketball game

Regularly, try to select a new idea. This keeps residents, staff and your administrator watching your calendar.

Community involvement and projects

List potential projects in these two columns:
- project with a local school
- party for underprivileged children
- develop a resident-tended flower garden

Then complete the *outings* and *cooking* columns. There you have a master sheet for a whole year of activities. Tack it prominently over your desk, or store it with your monthly planning calendar.

Planning the whole year

Once your master sheet is as complete as you can make it, take out your year-at-a-glance calendar. Using your completed master sheet, begin to pinpoint the desired activities into the proper month on the big calendar. You need not target a particular day yet; just jot them in blank spaces in that month. When you find a proper date, move it from the blank space into the correct day.

Let's first look at your *yearly* column. You see *pet show* listed. Ask, "Which month would be best for a pet show?" Since kids love their pets and like to show them off, and since they are probably bored with summer vacation by then, why not select July. Jot *pet show* on your big calendar in July. Then look at *queen contest.* What would be a good month? How about incorporating it into *National Nursing Home Week?* If that's your choice, pencil it on your full-year calendar in May. How about *baby-loving days?* Which month? With the holidays over, young Mom's may be feeling cooped up and need to get out in January. Invite them to bring their young children. Put that activity on your year-at-a-glance calendar. I'm sure you get the idea. We've already filled January, May and July. Continue on in the same way until you've placed your selected *yearly* activities on your big calendar.

Then choose another column from your master list. Let's try *occasionally.* Perhaps you want to hatch chicks. When? How about late April? Record it. Continue on through the *occasionally* list moving the activities into a particular month on the big calendar.

Next, transfer the *new ideas, community involvements,* and *special projects* into the selected months. When that's done, add in *monthly* activities: resident council, district activity directors' meetings, monthly Bible study and so on.

Then go to *seasonally* and transfer the holidays you wish to celebrate to the proper month. You do not have to fill in your *weekly* and *daily* activities. Church and regularly-scheduled weekly groups are pretty well set. These *can* be put on the big calendar if you choose; however, you may not want to schedule things like bingo and movies, hard and fast because they can always be moved to a different day if necessary. If these *daily* and *weekly* activities are listed on your master sheet, you will not forget to add them in each month as you plan your final calendar.

This large year-at-a-glance calendar lets you see if you have over-scheduled any activity. It allows you much variety in your activities and also incorporates exciting *new* activities into your program.

From one calendar to another

With this calendar as a reference, now take a regular desk-planning calendar. Go through each individual month and transfer the activities recorded on your year-at-a-glance calendar to the proper month on this smaller calendar. (This is the calendar you actually work from.) As you don't necessarily have an actual date for the events, just transfer them into the blank squares at this point. When the actual month rolls around, just move them into the date you choose. The big year-at-a-glance calendar is hung on the back of your office door or somewhere easily visible to you. When someone wants to know if you have a date open, or you wonder if you can fit a new idea into that month, a quick glance will tell you. And when it comes time for evaluation at the end of the year, simply roll up your big calendar and take it with you. Share it with your administrator. Should a raise be in question, it's an instant record of all you've accomplished that year.

Summary

No longer need you find yourself at the end of the month fretting over an unplanned calendar. When you open each new month, you'll know exactly what you're going to be doing for the next thirty days. All you need do is target an actual day for the pre-planned activities. Then fill in the regular weekly and daily events. Using this system, preparing the calendar is greatly simplified. If you find calendar planning a real chore, give this method a try and see if it doesn't take the sting out of staring at a blank calendar and wondering, "Where do I start?"

CHAPTER 5

Writing an Enticing
Press Release

Do you want to keep your facility's name in a positive light before the community? Do you want your workplace to be covered regularly in the newspaper? Do you want to turn on the evening news and see your residents involved in an exciting event that *you* planned?

It's not difficult to get good publicity. Most of the activities presented in this book have been featured in a large newspaper or on the local television station. An Indianapolis television station, sixty-five miles away, covered one activity. Another was picked up by United Press International, and some others were featured in national magazines.

One of your duties as a professional activity director is to bring regular publicity to your facility. Some of you have mastered this well but others are weak in this area. It's not that you don't try. Perhaps no one has ever shown you how. Many times your activities are great and worthy of coverage, but your press releases haven't done their job of hooking the media and getting them into your facility for a first-hand look. In this chapter we're going to look at some actual press releases and describe the results they have or haven't achieved and why. They can be used as a guideline for you to prepare your own.

A few basic guidelines

When promoting your activity to the press, write *press release* or *news release* near the top of the page. The release should ideally be no more than one page long. You want to hook your reader (who will be deciding if your event is worthy of coverage) in the first sentence. Think it out carefully. Present the most important information first, and work down to lesser details. Give the *who, what, when, where, why* and *how.* List a *contact person*, probably yourself, and a phone number. In the following press releases, the facility's name, address, phone number and contact person will appear only on the first one to avoid repetition. Try using colored paper when sending out press releases. It's less likely to be overlooked on someone's cluttered desk. They say a picture is worth a thousand words; why not add a little pertinent clip art?

Let's look at some sample press releases

ABC Nursing Home
123 Elm Street
Happyville, New York 12345
Contact: Your name, activity director
123-456-7890

PRESS RELEASE

They may not be swaddling clothes, and the babes are certainly not the Christ Child, but thirty stiff fingers have worked tirelessly since August hand-sewing flannel baby gowns so that every baby born during the holiday season can have one for his trip home from the hospital. Three residents from ABC Nursing Home have thoroughly enjoyed this project. With each tiny gown completed, they have visualized the infant who will wear it, worrying if it will fit, if the neck hole is too small, or if the lace will scratch the baby's delicate skin.

This has been an expensive project because quality materials have gone into each gown and because of the number being made-- so far sixty-eight--and they are still sewing. The gowns come in small, medium and large. In addition, extra small gowns are being made for the preemies in the neo-natal unit. To finance it, several ABC residents have worked for many months creating dolls from socks and dressing them in flannel gowns and bonnets and selling them to staff and visitors. With the six dollars earned for each doll, they have purchased thirty-five yards of fabric and ribbon and lace. The baby gowns will be presented to representatives from both hospitals who will be having lunch at ABC with residents and department heads. If you'd like to stop by and cover the feature for a warm human interest story, I'm sure residents would be happy to show off their creations. You can reach me at ABC between 8:00 a.m. and 4:00 p.m. weekdays.

*(This activity was featured on the T.V. evening news and was published in the hospital's newsletter. In addition, it was published in **Lady's Circle** magazine. The magazine feature, though, required a different letter called a "proposal" to sell it to them.)*

PRESS RELEASE

Dear Jack (newspaper daily columnist),

If any mother had a baby born at one of the local hospitals this past Christmas season or attended one of ABC's "baby loving days" about two years ago, they might have a little celebrity on their hands. The only problem is: *I don't know who these babies are or where to reach their parents.*

Enclosed find a copy of January's *Lady's Circle* magazine that hits the newsstands this week. In it you will find an article about ABC's various outreaches to our community. One of those outreaches, you will no doubt remember, was the making of seventy-five baby gowns for all the babies born at the hospitals last Christmas season. One of the pictures featured is of local babies modeling the gowns made by residents. Another picture is of three babies visiting the nursing home. I'm sure the mothers would be proud to see their little ones featured in a national magazine, but they need to be informed. I don't know if you might want to do something on this or not, but I felt you were a good place to start.

Thanks,

Marge Knoth, activity director

(This story was run in the newspaper man's column, giving us two stories plus T.V. coverage from the same activity.)

PRESS RELEASE

Dear Jack,

Ever heard of a plant hospital? We haven't either, but it seems we have one here at ABC.

I suppose you've noticed our new all-glass sunroom from Elm Street. In the short time we've had it, plants we've had for years have shown remarkable growth. Recently, my married daughter returned to me a plant I'd given her and said, "It won't grow at my house." We brought it to the "plant hospital" at ABC, and it's on its way back to health. Then came the idea! Maybe we could help others in the community who have failing plants as well as those who need a plant-sitter while going on vacation. Residents thoroughly enjoy looking at the assortment of plants, and a few like to tenderly care for them under the direction of a staff member. We're not asking any money for this service, but if anyone wishes to make a donation, it will go to the activity fund for buying planters and soil. We can't guarantee anything in the plant hospital except lots of love and care to each and every plant.

At ABC, we're always seeking ways to keep residents in touch with their community and trying to find ways in which they can reach out and give, in spite of their age and handicaps. This is one such project that gives residents a chance to serve. We weren't sure how to go about getting the word out to the public about what we'd like to do for the community, but then I thought of you. If you'd like to do a story, feel free to call.

Marge Knoth, activity director

(This brought a story in the newspaper with the result being lots of new plants for the nursing home. A nursery donated about a hundred plants. Some left their plants for the winter while they went to Florida.)

PRESS RELEASE

Though the temperature outside registers ninety-plus degrees, residents of ABC Nursing Home are keeping quite cool planning to celebrate Christmas--Christmas in July, that is. In December, Christmas in a nursing home is almost too hectic to be enjoyed with the frenzy of activity--carollers in number, parties, special guests, and family visits. July, on the other hand, is slower, more relaxed and provides lots of time for planning and enjoying. So...

Monday, July 20: Residents will decorate the Christmas tree.

Tuesday, July 21: Residents will enjoy a reminiscence group about Christmas long ago. Candy will be made.

Wednesday, July 22: Captain Smith, of the Salvation Army, will lead residents in singing Christmas carols. He'll bring kids to share a party with residents. (Laughingly, he volunteered to bring his bell and kettle.) Mr. and Mrs. Santa will visit.

Thursday, July 23: We'll center on the religious meaning of

Christmas with a Christmas message from a local
pastor.

Friday, July 24: We'll feature Christmas movies, and then
residents will enjoy taking down the tree.

It should be a fun time for everyone, so if you'd like to cover any of
our activities this week, give me a call.

*(This feature brought the television station to our facility where they
filmed the residents decorating the Christmas tree and clowning around,
putting Santa hats on each other. One resident even played his harmonica
for the cameraman. This was featured on the evening news.)*

PRESS RELEASE

It's not often a nursing home patient enrolls in college, but that's
just what happened with one of ABC's residents. Sally Johnson
accepted the challenge when it was offered by Purdue University.
Though she'll probably never earn a degree, the willingness to learn
is certainly present. She has enrolled in an outreach program for the
home-bound. She will go to Purdue for orientation and for one
class; then her other lessons will be taught via television by a Purdue
associate. The course Sally will be taking is called "The Write
Course." Sally is the only nursing home resident in the area who will
be working on this project for college credit.

If you would like to talk to Sally about her venture, she would
be delighted to share her attempt with you. Feel free to contact me
here days between 8:00 A.M. and 4:00 P.M.

(This press release brought television coverage on the evening news.)

PRESS RELEASE

Dear Jack,

Something happened at ABC Nursing Home recently that I think might make a cute human interest story. Most of your newspaper employees who park in the North Street lot are familiar with resident John Jansen who always sits outside ABC and greets them as they pass by.

A few months ago here at the nursing home, another resident was dying, and I went into his room to comfort him. He wanted me to pray with him. John Jansen, his roommate, came rolling into the room at that moment and was so touched by the situation that he reached out his hand wanting to pray with us. A third resident followed John into the room and also wanted to pray. The dying man, on his deathbed, made his peace with God. John and the other resident did the same. From that moment on, **John** Jansen had a real change of heart. He became spiritually **hungry and** wanted to hear every minister, and every visitor who would, **talk about** God. He wanted the Bible read to him regularly. John has **had** a stroke, and although his mind is alert and active, speaking is difficult for him; he can say only a few words. Somehow, with John's limited vocabulary, he got the message across to me that he was a Catholic; but because years ago, he joined a secret organization, he was asked to leave his church. We took this issue to the priest who holds our Thursday morning Mass. The priest said things had changed and began to give John communion right along with the rest of the Catholics. Then one day I received a call from John's son who rarely visited asking if John had received his First Communion. It was at this point that John's son told me that John *was not and never had been a Catholic*. In fact, he had never been a church-going man at all. And he had never even been baptized. When we talked to John about this, he admitted it and let us know he wanted to be baptized. "Would you like a minister to come into the facility and baptize you?" I asked.

41

"No!" he shouted loudly and forcefully, pointing to the Catholic Church close by. He wanted to be baptized in the Catholic Church.

And so that's exactly what happened! Thirty-four school children, along with their teachers, showed up at the nursing home and pushed several of our residents across the bumpy street and parking lot to St. Boniface Church. They lined residents in wheel chairs up in front of the altar, and they sat down in the pews behind them. John's son and his son's wife joined them. The priest performed the ceremony of baptism on seventy-five years old John as big tears rolled down his cheeks. During the ceremony, the kids sang songs welcoming John into the Christian family. Each one made him an original card and congratulated him before returning him and the other residents to the facility.

That afternoon ABC residents held a party complete with balloons, cake and punch to celebrate the grand occasion. The school kids came again and were going to sing *Congratulations to You* but didn't know how, so they sang *Happy Birthday* which was appropriate anyway because it was indeed his spiritual birthday. John received a plaque and a cross from his family, and the nursing home gave him a cross on a chain to replace the rosary he had been wearing around his neck since he gave his heart to the Lord Jesus.

Throughout the party, tears kept spilling over as John's heart was so tenderly touched. At the reception, each child read his card to John, and he cried some more. All the residents and staff spent John's baptismal day rejoicing with him. Just thought you might be interested.

Marge Knoth, activity director

(You will notice this letter is much longer than a press release should be, but upon examining it, you will also notice that it not your typical press release. The event had already happened, and I was seeking after-the-fact publicity which is usually next to impossible to get. Yet the story peaked the newspaper man's curiosity, and he wrote a column about the interesting mix-up with the happy ending.)

PRESS RELEASE

You could fix them with a hairpin, they say, and when they were cranked, you'd better watch out, or you'd break your arm. Yes, that old Model-T with the big brass radiator and the brass carbide gas lights that were so erratic, holds a special memory in our residents' hearts. They courted in that old car, rode their babies around in it, and remember their doctors' driving it. To bring back pleasant memories and to celebrate *National Nursing Home Week,* a Model-T club will bring three or four cars to ABC for residents to admire, to sit in, and maybe even to go for a ride. One resident who once owned Model-T's is already dreaming of cruising around the downtown square in one of them.

> **Where:** ABC Nursing Home
> 123 Elm Street
> Happyville, New York 12345
> **When:** Monday, May 12, 1986
> **Time:** 1:00 - 3:00

If you would like to come and see this love affair with old cars unfold, feel free to join us.

(This one did not bring a story. Probably because old car shows are too common.)

PRESS RELEASE

If you should wander into ABC Nursing Home in the month of December, you'll very likely find Santa's elves (ages 71-92) working frantically to meet their December 21st deadline.

ABC's administrator has built a sturdy plywood Barbie doll house (4' x 1-1/2' x 3-1/2'), and residents are busy furnishing it. They're choosing just the right wallpaper and carpeting from donated samples, and they are hand-sewing draperies and crocheting rugs. They're sanding and painting furniture made from small blocks of two-by-fours, and they are busy gluing tiny rocks on styrofoam to create a three-story-tall fireplace. Miniature lamps, flower arrangements and pictures for the wall are being constructed. Dolls will be purchased, and the house will be furnished down to the dishes on the table.

Through the month of December, ABC will welcome children into the facility to sign up to try and win the house. It will be given away on Friday, December 21st in a drawing. All it takes to be eligible is for a child, twelve or under, to come in and shake the hand of one resident. If he or she is shy, though, a pretty smile will do. Our residents love kids, and this will allow them the thrill of seeing the little ones and also let them share with the children all about the house they are creating.

We hope this will be a great interaction between the old and the young. We want the project to brighten our residents spirits a little by having something to *give,* rather than just always being on the receiving end.

If you would like to see our house or get a picture or a story, feel free to call weekdays between 8:00 a.m. and 3:00 p.m.

(This activity brought a nice picture story. A resident was photographed reaching through a miniature window and picking up a table.)

PRESS RELEASE

Dear Jack,

How would you like an interview with a real live cowboy and his wife who helped settle the Old West back in 1907?

"Going out west then via train and riding it around dangerous edges of mountain ranges was an adventure in itself," says Bertha Linson (see cover photo) the cowboy's wife and now a resident of ABC Nursing Home. Cowboys in those days didn't have a nice shiny horse as in the movies. They just picked up a wild range horse to do their work of rounding up and herding cattle.

"Sometimes you got a good one" says Opel, the cowboy, "and sometimes you got a dud. I bought a rope horse once. I didn't know he hadn't been ridden. I put a saddle on him and got on. In two or three jumps I was on the ground. Someone later said, 'Why didn't you hit the saddle horn?' I said, 'I couldn't find it.'"

Opel carried a side arm, just like the movie cowboys--a Colt 45--but not to protect himself from *black hat* cowboys. It was to defend against rattlesnakes, mountain lions and other wild animals. Cowboys slept on the ground.

There was no minimum wage, he recalls. You got your clothes and your board. He remembers that one generous rancher paid his cowboys thirty dollars a month plus a house, beef, and access to fruit trees and garden space. Cowboys workdays started at daybreak and ended when darkness came.

In 1917 Opel married Bertha. He was eighteen; she was fifteen. For a time, they lived out of a covered wagon. They remember when telephone lines were simply barbed wired strung across the top of fence posts. She tells that there really were cowboys who wore white hats. Once she and Opel were out in a touring car that had no top. It began to rain. The car stalled and they were stranded. A Cowboy came by, tied a rope to their radiator cap and pulled them into town.

On Christmas eve, this delightful couple will celebrate their 70th wedding anniversary. Might you be interested?

Marge Knoth, activity director

(This prolific newspaper columnist, who does most interviews via telephone, rushed right over to our facility to personally interview this couple. He wrote a nice column about them complete with their picture.)

PRESS RELEASE
The *Pan-Am Torch Run* signaling the approaching opening of the PAN-AM games in Indianapolis will pass through Lafayette

about noon on Sunday, July 19. The torch will be carried by local runners, but one torch carrier won't be running! She'll be riding in a wheel chair. Sixty-nine year old Vivian Eaton, a stroke patient with the use of only one arm and one leg, is anxiously looking forward to her ride. She'll hold the torch high for one mile while doing her part to raise money for the *Riley Children's Hospital* in Indianapolis.

Each runner (rider) must be sponsored by someone willing to donate $100 to the cause. ABC Nursing Home is Vivian's sponsor. She will be pushed her mile by its administrator and owner, Richard Linson. Each torch runner will receive a tee-shirt and shorts. Vivian, a fun-loving lady with a great sense of humor, is willing to wear the T-shirt, but she's still considering the shorts.

Just sitting on ABC's patio soaking up sun is invigorating for Vivian, so when an opportunity for a real outing--especially one that would help raise money for a good cause--came her way, she jumped at the chance and hasn't stopped glowing yet.

I can't help feeling this has the makings of a good human interest story, so if you're interested, feel free to give me a call.

(They were interested. She was featured on the front page of the newspaper, on the local television news, and the feature was replayed for several days. In addition, the Indianapolis television station also traveled to Lafayette for this one and featured it on their news and several other spots as well.)

PRESS RELEASE

Santa arrived at ABC Nursing Home for the annual Christmas party with a very unusual gift. Rather than the usual shaving lotion, nylons and jewelry, as he opened his big sack, *what to the wondering eyes of residents did appear,* but a doll baby that looked, oh, so real. Santa would not leave her, though, until he had a solemn promise from ABC residents that she would indeed be adopted by them and loved forevermore. He also insisted that she would be rocked and cradled and allowed to take naps in the residents rooms.

It was a tough decision at first. With all their children and grandchildren reared, did they have yet what it would take to become parents at their age? Could forty-five senior citizens in their seventies, eighties, and nineties jointly share the parenthood of one lovable, round-faced baby doll? The resident council debated. Then the baby doll was brought out. First one, then another loved her. She was the next best thing to a real live baby.

It was a decision no longer. In spite of any obstacle, she now had a home at 123 Elm Street with not merely a mama and a papa to love her, but lots and lots of grandparents to spoil little *Bev Cammie ABC*. The big rocking chair was brought out to the dining room for Cammie's daily rocking.

An official adoption party is planned Friday, December 28, at 1:30 at ABC. Adoption papers will be filed after being signed by a resident council member and each resident will take the oath of adoption. As guest of honor, little Bev Cammie will be inviting all her sister and brother Cabbage Patch kids in the Lafayette area to come with their young *Mamas* for ice cream and cake, balloons and prizes.

Santa found *Cabbage Patch* Cammie on the store shelves and thought of all the Grandmas and Grandpas at ABC. So into his bag she went! Today, little Bev Cammie is as happy as can be in her ABC home. Feel free to stop by or call for further information.

(This feature, also an after-the-fact story, was not picked up on by the media, probably because the Cabbage Patch phase was on its way out. Yet thirty-five Cabbage Patch dolls with their little mothers and grandmothers came for a fantastic party which was great public relations--even if we didn't get a story.)

PRESS RELEASE

Monday, nineteen eager little faces, some no bigger than a minute, sat encircling the piano played by an ABC volunteer. They sang *Rudolph* and *Silent Night.* Joyful little voices mingled with the shaky voices of nursing home residents. Kids expectantly awaited the arrival of a jolly old man in a red suit. Soon jingle bells rang, and the little ones snapped to attention upon hearing the familiar "Ho! Ho! Ho!" Instead of setting to work passing out gifts, Santa, after greeting everyone--old folks, young folks and those in between--pulled up a big chair and asked the kids a question.

"Do you know who my very, most special friend is?"

"Rudolph!" many of them yelled in unison.

"Wrong!" chuckled Santa.

"It's Jesus! And I have such a good story to tell you about Him that I am going to read it from a book to see that I get it just right."

Three little ones, two and three-year-olds, stood in awe before Santa throughout the whole story of the first Christmas. Then Santa turned his eyes on the tree, and the nineteen underprivileged children who were guests of the nursing home residents raced to it knowing that there was a grocery bag full of wrapped presents for each one of them beneath it. Santa, with sheer delight written all over his face, held the little ones on his lap as he passed out the presents. A resident distributed to each little guest, a six pack of donated cola. The sound of paper tearing filled the ABC activity room as one after another child opened their packages.

"Tube socks!" one yelled. "Now I won't have to wear my brother's." A tiny little girl then proudly modeled her new knitted hat. The socks, hats, mittens and a toy were generously provided by donations from the Kiwanas, Rotary, Moose and the nursing home. The children seemed every bit as delighted with their hats and socks as they did with the many donated toys.

After the excitement of opening presents, the children feasted on grapes, tangerines, oranges, crackers, cheese and cola. When the

48

kid's finished eating, they helped serve the nursing home residents who were in wheel chairs and unable to get to the table. Then resident, Myrtle James, passed out donated plastic stockings filled with candy. Each of them received fruit donated by a local super-market. Finally a new one dollar bill was presented to each child. One child remarked, "Wow, I never had this much money in my life!"

As the party progressed, there was quite a racket with toy trucks and cars racing everywhere, but residents were enjoying it as much as the kids. Some little ones chose not to open their gifts. Possibly they were saving them so they'd have something under their own tree on Christmas morning.

Finally it was over, and the kids all loaded in the van that would take them back to the community center from which they came. Many happy faces peered from the van windows waving to their new-found old friends. The happy youngsters had just come to realize that there really was a Santa Claus--one who not only brings presents to them, but who tells them of Jesus, his best friend, who was born in a manger of that first Christmas day.

(This is another "after the fact" press release. For some reason, the newspaper didn't pick up on it when I first announced the party, but they ran a feature about it from this release after the party was over.)

Summary

One of the first lessons a writer learns is: *Show them, don't tell them.* In that same vein, these press releases have been included to show you how to get media coverage for your facility. You, as activity director, have at your fingertips, the makings of numerous news stories. Sometimes you just have to look for them. With the old cowboy couple, I wanted to get a story about their 70th wedding anniversary, but I suspected it would be just a picture and an announcement. They were such special people, and I wanted something more for them. So I began to look for an *angle* or a *peg* to hang the story on. Then I remembered the stories Opel liked to tell about the West, and I used the *cowboy* angle. Not only was their anniversary announced, but they received a good feature story about themselves that they still treasure.

A newspaperman, who covered one of my first activities, (the forming of our basketball team), gave me some invaluable advice.

"Don't bother us with run of the mill stories but if you have something new or different, give us a call. If you don't have something new or different, put new twist on an old idea."

And that's what we did with the basketball game mentioned above. In itself, playing basketball is not necessarily newsworthy-- unless it is a well-known team or a championship game. But when eighty and ninety-year-olds begin to play basketball and challenge other facilities, that's a story! This activity netted our facility a three-page spread in the magazine section of our Sunday newspaper. The reporter's advice is probably the best an activity director can receive on the subject.

Press coverage is not difficult to obtain. Just find a good story and write a tempting press release. Hook your reader in the first sentence and then work down to the lesser details. Mail your press release out in plenty of time--ten days to two weeks before your activity. Sometimes you can get coverage with a phone call to the press, but a written press release is more effective. Even written releases need to be followed up with a phone call the day before your activity. Begin to work on first-quality press releases, and soon you'll be able to fill a scrapbook with news stories about your facility. Before you know it, your facility will stand out in the community among all the others, and once again, you'll be recognized for the professional activity director you really are.

CHAPTER 6

Reaching Out
To Your Community

Would you like your activity program to be positively talked about by the whole city? It's a big order to fill. It would be next to impossible for an administrator, D.O.N, dietician or aide to do; but you, as a professional activity director, can make it happen. The trick is to regularly involve your community in your activity program. Keep them guessing what's coming next. By doing this you not only lift your facility's name in the public's eye but the image of long-term care facilities in general. Let's explore a few activity ideas that will bring the community into your facility and keep them talking about it.

Celebrity day

Make a list of interesting community people to invite. Include as many as possible who wear a uniform. This adds color and makes the event more impressive. Here's some celebrity suggestions:

- scout leaders
- Boy Scouts
- Girl Scouts
- Brownies
- priest, bishop, minister
- city clerk
- political candidates
- cheerleaders
- radio disc jockey
- recruiters: Army, Navy, Air Force, and Marine
- state representative
- mayor
- policeman
- fireman (and fire dog)
- judge
- auditor
- sports figures: high school or college
- newspaper editor
- television anchor
- Arthur Murray dancers

Let your imagination run free and you'll come up with many more. To begin your list, open your phone book to *city of* (your city's name) or *county of* (your county's name). Involve your residents in the excitement of the coming event. Let them help make name tags-- perhaps crown-shaped ones for guests and star-shaped tags for themselves. Decorate in patriotic red, white and blue. Display an American flag. Plan simple refreshments like cookies and punch or crackers and cheese. Try to limit the event to an hour or so.

The agenda is simple. Guests, on arrival, sign in and personally greet each resident. Then they help themselves to refreshments. Planned entertainment is not needed though you may wish to have your cheerleaders perform or dancers demonstrate a couple of numbers. For the most part, guests quickly become involved with the residents and that *is* the entertainment. Finally, try to obtain media coverage. If you have already invited a newspaperman or T.V. personality as a guest, you shouldn't have any trouble.

This activity serves several purposes: one, it involves the community; two, it's flattering to guests to be recognized as celebrities; three, it makes your residents feel important to have interesting people visiting them; and four, it will usually get you good press coverage.

Pet Show

This can become a yearly event. July is a good time to hold it. Not only are kids are out of school, but by then parents are anxious for their kids to have something fun to do.

Announce it using any available free community events advertising. In the past, though, I've noticed most response does not come from these sources. Even so, you are keeping your facility's name positively before the public. It announces that your facility is interested in its community and is offering it something. Next, if you have a local park zoo or an animal shelter, ask them to bring pets. Invite nursery schools and senior citizens centers to bring their pets. And, lastly, ask staff and friends. Usually, as many adults come to show off their pets as do children.

The object is to try and find a category so that every pet receives an award. Little silver and gold painted plastic trophies can be purchased very inexpensively and given for prizes. You might want to give ribbons for second place. These can either be purchased or hand made from funeral ribbons.

Set up a head table and appoint three to five residents to sit behind it as judges. Make them each a prominent name tag that reads "judge." On the front of the table where they are sitting, tape signs for each category. They might read:

- smallest dog
- largest animal
- best-behaved
- cutest
- friendliest
- largest dog
- smartest animal
- liveliest
- strongest
- most mischievous

On the judges table, have a sign up list for each categories. Guests can register their pet in any category or even several.

If you have a microphone, it's best to hook it up near the judges' table. One by one, have guests bring their pet up and tell a little about it. Let them then present their pet to the judge for a first-hand look. When all pets have been shown, let the judges decide who wins in each category. This will usually take your help. Residents know the ones they like but are often unable to do the paper work. A volunteer may do this for you.

You can try for publicity but this event is fairly common. Still, if the media are in need of a story or have a two-minute spot on the end of the evening news to fill, they may be looking for such a story. Even if they don't pick up on it, you've already gotten free publicity by advertising it.

County Fair

Many residents are unable to go to the county fair, but that's no reason the fair can't come to them. It takes some planning, but this can be a highly successful event. It brings the community into your facility as well as the press who are constantly looking for a timely, yet unusual story.

Begin planning early. Contact your local 4-H office or county Home Extension office and share your idea. They will usually work with you and inform the various 4-H clubs or give you the names of the clubs to contact. Plan your event for the week immediately following the real 4-H fair. Invite 4-H kids and adults from the community to bring in their fair projects. Also invite adults and children not involved in 4-H who have projects they'd like to exhibit. Some sample entries might include:

- model airplanes
- crafts
- baby pig
- prized vegetables and fruits
- cakes and pies
- quilts
- furniture projects
- canned goods
- rabbits
- leaf collection

Set up several tables to accommodate all the items. Give prizes if you wish though they are not necessary. This is basically a *demonstration* of projects and animals. Have each person come forward and tell a little about his particular entry. Serve simple refreshments.

This event need not last all day but just an hour or two. Your community will love it. The press will love it. And your residents will especially love it since the county fair was the highlight of the year in days gone by. Many pleasant memories will be revived.

Basketball game with the pros

If you have a college in your area, here's an activity that will not only be fun, but will bring your facility great publicity. If you don't have a college, you could play ball with a high school team.

Contact the coach. In a big university, it may take a little doing, but be persistent. It can be done. Call the college basketball arena to locate the coach, or better yet, contact the public relations person who handles the team's publicity. It's best to schedule your game at the end of the team's season or before it starts. The coach may choose to come with just three or four players which is fine. For the residents' benefit, ask them to wear some school identification such as a shirt with the school's name on it.

Play a nursing-home basketball game (see page 162) with the coach and his team. Seat them on one side of the circle as team one, and your residents on the other side of the circle as team two. This game was played at my facility with coach Gene Keady and his Purdue Boilermakers. Needless to say, the press ate it up and gave us a front page story in our newspaper.

Baby-loving day

Baby-loving day developed from the traditional *baby contest.* The problem with baby contests is that the residents get so involved in *judging* the babies that they never get a chance to do what they want most--just to hug them and love them.

This event can be held successfully about four times a year. First, advertise it in the community events column of your newspaper and on public service announcements. Also, promote it on the bulletin boards at your facility, and spread the word to families of residents. Before the babies (birth to kindergarten) arrive, have your residents, either in wheel chairs or regular chairs, form a large circle. When the babies come, have a few toys--balls, bucket to put them in, bean bags, etc.--in the circle. The mothers will usually sit down on the floor with the kids in the circle for a few minutes to get them interested in playing. Before you know it, the babies are crawling up on the laps of residents. Mothers place the younger babies in residents' arms to love.

Refreshments, given with the mothers' permission, of course, might be animal cookies and juice. It's also nice to have lots of colorful balloons around for the kids to play with and take home. Spend your time visiting with the mothers and building good rapport. You are the image they are getting of your facility. As you talk informally with them, it's a good time to ask if they'd like to leave their names and addresses so you can inform them of the next baby-loving day. This event is so successful that mothers will probably be calling you to ask when you are going to have it again.

Even if you have a long list of mothers who want to come, still announce your event in the public service columns to keep your facility's name before the community. They will see you are doing fun things for residents and may consider you, if and when, they need a long-term-care facility.

Other ideas

Ideas are numerous to involve residents and community. You might try renting a famous 16mm movie such as *Old Yeller* or another children's movie and invite the public in to view it. Set up your activity room like a theater with rows of chairs. Be sure to serve free popcorn. When you rent a movie, check, because some film companies won't let you use the actual title in promoting your event.

You might hold an Easter egg hunt for your community or have a talent or doll show. Since ladies like to show off their quilts, why not hold a quilt show? This can be promoted into a big event.

If you have the room, consider letting community groups hold their meetings at your facility. These could include scout troops, clubs or various organizations. More than likely these groups will feel indebted to you and think first of your facility when they do a service project.

You might invite a garden club in to turn a bleak spot into a flower garden or landscaped area for residents to view and enjoy. Allow them to place a small marker or sign indicating the name of their group as having done the landscaping.

In summertime, residents can break green beans or shuck corn for community people who don't have the time to do it themselves. This has been a very successful activity because residents feel useful in doing something that was once a big part of their lives. Even confused residents enjoy this project. Use free advertising to announce residents would be happy to break green beans for community people while they work and that they can pick them up after work. This brings the community into your facility. Don't ask for any reward. Just chalk it up to good will. If you should advertise and no one responds, it doesn't matter. You have still gotten free publicity for your facility.

Summary

These are but a few ideas to help you involve your community, but they are tried and true ones that work. You'll find more community outreaches that are especially for Christmas in Chapter thirteen. The important thing is to keep your facility's name visible. As people come into your facility for these programs and you personally visit with them, they'll feel welcome and positive about your facility. They'll also come to recognize you as the professional activity director your really are.

CHAPTER 7

Activities + Families
= Good Will

One sure way to get residents' families strongly backing your activity program is to involve them in it. Of course family members visit their loved ones in their rooms, but that is not the same as them attending social affairs together. Even though *you* are doing most of the work, residents delight in assuming the role of host or hostess to their families as they attend special activities together in your facility. And that is as it should be. It is their home. Residents' families are their honored guests. These functions serve not only to give both residents and families an enjoyable evening, but they also provide an opportunity for excellent public relations. Doing something extra special for the families leaves them thinking and talking positively about your facility. If your administrator doesn't see the value of investing in this type of activity, challenge him to allow you to hold one activity for residents and families--a meal and entertainment--and to come and view the results first hand. If he takes up your challenge, more than likely, he will be convinced of the good will it brings and realize that the expense is a small price to pay for the benefits derived.

Four resident/family events a year work out well. If there are too many, families quickly tire of them. If there are too few, chances are some families may never get to one. You and your administrator must determine *who* family actually involves--children? grandchildren? brothers and sisters? special friends of residents without families? (We left ours open to any family member or friend who made a reservation.) Be prepared, though, because there are always those who show up without ever letting you know they're coming. This is not a problem unless it's a family of ten, and you are short of seating. When an activity involves a *meal* rather than just *snacks,* the turn out is much greater. Unfortunately, a facility cannot continually feed unlimited guests, so it's wise to alternate the family meal activities with parties offering just refreshments. Let's take a look at some activities that have proven successful in the past.

Thanksgiving dinner

Held about Monday of Thanksgiving week, this one usually provides an excellent turnout. You will need to work closely with your administrator on cost and direction, and with and your kitchen who will probably be preparing the food. If so, have your facility provide the turkey, dressing, gravy, a vegetable and drinks. Let each family bring a salad or dessert. This is not an imposition. For some reason, they love to carry in their special recipes. Line a couple of long tables at the front of the room for the food your facility provides and as many other tables as are needed for the guests' contributions. Long narrow tables and folding chairs can often be borrowed from a nearby school. You might push several of these tables together end-to-end, and make three, four or more long lines of connecting tables. It goes without saying that you want to leave plenty of room between the rows of tables for wheel chairs and guests to maneuver comfortably. For most activities, it's attractive to cover the tables in a red and white checked paper or plastic covering. This can be purchased from a party-goods store or a paper supply business. Use appropriate centerpieces. To have a maximum number of guests, six o'clock is generally a good time to hold it.

Have families fill plates for their resident, and it will be up to facility workers to serve those who are left. Hopefully aides will serve their patients at the activity, but you may not be able to count on it, depending on the cooperation in your facility. It's always wise to bring in some volunteers. Even a willing husband and children can help a lot by seeing that residents are served and various needs are met.

The meal, itself, is a wonderful opportunity for gathering together, but to give your residents and guests a really good time, plan some entertainment, also. A band or barbershop quartet or similar entertainment is good here because carrying it out requires little effort on your part. You will have your hands full with the many other details of the activity without having to personally entertain. Because of residents' sometimes limited attention span, the entertainment after the meal should last little more than an hour. It's better that everyone leaves wanting more than simply waiting for the event to end.

Oktoberfest

If you have a German band or know someone who entertains German style, this activity is a sure winner. Again, invite families for a real German dinner and entertainment. Have bowls of pretzels setting on the tables so guests can munch while waiting for dinner. The meal might consist of bratwurst and sauerkraut, dark rolls, a vegetable, spiced apples and raisins, black forest cake and drinks. Or you could have the guests bring the dessert and the salads.

Let your entertainment perform for about an hour after the meal. This activity can easily become a yearly event, but it's best when rotated every other year with the Thanksgiving dinner. If you missed having an Oktoberfest, you may wish to have the same thing later and call it a *winterfest* or a *summerfest.*

Cake walk

This can be a fun activity. Ask guests to each bring a cake. Leave the center of the floor clear and make a winding road on the floor with large sheets of paper. Each sheet must have a number on it. Number all cakes with the same numbers as those on the floor. Have guests, and residents who are able, take part in the cake walk. For each particular walk, set one cake out to be won. Just like musical chairs, play music. When it stops, the one who is standing on the same number as the cake is the winner of that cake.

This activity alone is seldom enough for an evening's entertainment. It might be held halfway through some other entertainment such as a band playing, a singer singing or a child performing.

Pie social

Pie socials were popular long ago, and senior citizens love them. Have each family bring a pie and slice it. Provide lots of ice cream and whipped cream, and let guests serve themselves and their resident. This can be an activity in itself or held in conjunction with other simple entertainment. You might want to let residents entertain a little, or perhaps you could show off some of their crafts or sewing projects, and even offer them for sale.

Cook out and old car show

In summer, this activity often goes over well. Maybe you could convince your administrator to act as chef and fry hamburgers. Perhaps you want to do it up a little bigger and have a hog roast.

It all depends on your budget. Plan for emergencies such as rain. Have ready a room large enough to accommodate everyone should it be necessary to move inside. Invite a Model-T or old-time car club to bring cars to your facility. Clubs will often do this at no cost to you. Many memories are brought back as residents and families study the cars, both before and after the cookout.

The roaring Twenties

This is a fun party. If you or someone else enjoys dressing up, wear a roaring Twenties outfit--short sack dress with long beads and a band around your head. Invite entertainment in who sing Twenties music. Read up a little on the Twenties, and talk with guests about the fashions, fads, news happenings, movies, movie stars and the songs. Invite residents and guests to reminisce. Ask about prohibition, speakeasies, flag-pole sitting, dance-a-thons and the stock market crash. Serve snacks. You probably wouldn't want to ask guests to bring food unless a meal is being served.

Gay Nineties

Some residents or their parents lived in this era. Your local museum may loan you costumes of the era or may even put on a fashion show for you. Find pictures of the gay Nineties, and hang them on the walls. Calendars, gotten in December or January from a party supply business, sometimes have pretty girls dressed in the gay-Nineties fashion. Display on tables or hang on walls, photographs of people who lived in the gay Nineties. Gather all the antiques you can find--shoe buttoners, oil lamps, old kitchen utensils, old tools, churns and spinning wheels, and set up a display table for guests and residents to view and reminisce. Find a band or group who sings music from that era.

When the group who was entertaining for this event came to my facility, they told me they had planned a Minnie Pearl auction. They brought a real auctioneer in for it. I told them that was fine never considering what they *would auction off. Halfway through the event when I had stepped out of the activity area, I heard everyone calling me. I went in and found that I was to be auctioned off. For $10,000 (play money), I was bought by a fun-loving patient who outbid all the others. He never let me forget that he bought me. You might want to try a humorous auction of some sort, but hopefully you won't get caught as I did.*

Mother-daughter-granddaughter-great-granddaughter tea

This can be done anytime, but it's nice near Mother's Day. Give corsages (inexpensively purchased ones or tissue flowers made by residents) to every lady in attendance. Ask each mother to tell her name, and age, if she will, and how many children, grandchildren, and great-grandchildren she has. Give prizes for the most descendants. Also, honor the oldest and youngest woman present. Make this one a little more fancy since it's just for the ladies. Use white table cloths and nice glass dishes and cups if you can get them. Find pretty table napkins. You may want to have the mayor's wife, a minister's wife or a prominent woman speak on motherhood or some subject ladies would enjoy. Plan special treats for the younger children. You may want to ask the ladies if they remember when women first gained the right to vote in 1919. Ask if they remember the first time they voted, and ask who the President was then. Ask if any remember why women wore yellow flowers on their lapels back then. (It was a sign that they were for the cause--women winning the right to vote.) This activity need last only an hour or so and can still be special to all who attend.

Luau

From travel bureaus, you can often get big posters of Hawaii to use for decorations. Draw life-size palm trees on blank newspaper print and hang them on the walls. String paper lanterns from the ceiling. Buy or make leis. (These can be made from funeral bouquet ribbons by sewing large stitches down the middle of the ribbons and simply gathering them.) Station a couple of residents at the door to give one to each guest on arrival.

For refreshments, hollow out a watermelon, and fill it with watermelon and cantaloupe balls, grapes, bananas and pineapple. Have some whole pineapples on the food table for decorations. Banana bread might be served, and also cheese. If you choose to make this a meal, you might want to serve roast pork.

Entertainment could be Hawaiian dancers. If you have a university nearby, they might well have an International Center who will provide dancers. Short of that, play Hawaiian music on tape. You may wish to show a movie about Hawaii which your guests will enjoy. These can be obtained from Modern Talking Pictures free-loan program (see page 161). Or perhaps you know someone who has taken home movies or slides of their trip to Hawaii. Ask them to share them at your party. Another possibility is to ask someone from the travel agency speak on Hawaii. By the time the evening is over, hopefully residents and guests will feel like they have had an exciting vacation.

Western night

Plan a western night for families. First, secure three or four bales of hay or straw for effect. Contact square dancers to come in for entertainment. When they take a break, let them sit on the bales of hay or straw. Families and residents seem to love square dancing, so you probably would not want to have a meal served with this activity. You could wear a denim skirt or jeans and a cowboy hat. Perhaps you could get men's red handkerchiefs for the male residents to wear around their necks. Serve simple refreshments. Let the dancers dance, and just sit back and enjoy with your residents and guests.

Christmas party

Christmas is a busy time, so begin planning and getting your invitations out early. You may wish to give a party for grandchildren and great-grandchildren of residents. You could show a children's Christmas movie--16mm or video--that can be borrowed from your library. You might read them, *The First Christmas*. Perhaps the little ones could act it out in play form wearing simple costumes.

You may wish to have an adult party just for the immediate families of residents. It could be an evening party or an afternoon tea. Somehow evening activities seem better attended. A good Christmas movie could be shown to the adults, also. You might have a tasting party where they could sample many Christmas treats. You could ask each guest to bring a plate of Christmas cookies or candy so there will be a variety. Everyone can then take some of each home. This party probably will be best attended if it is held early in Christmas week.

Summary

Family involvement is well worth every dollar that goes into it. Planning these events is a big job for any activity director. First, there's preparing an interesting invitation. For these, you could use clip-art (see page 161) and rub off letters (purchased at any office supply store), if you are not fortunate enough to have a computer graphics program at your disposal. Then there's securing entertainment, and there is planning for food and seeing to decorations. Finally, there seems to be a thousand little details that demand attention. By the time the party is upon you, you'll think you can't go on another minute; but the next thing you know, the room is full of residents and guests who are laughing and telling you what a great party it is. Suddenly you'll get a second wind that will carry you through till it's over and only the clean-up remains. Generally some families stick around and help fold up tables and chairs and discard tablecloths. If you are really blessed, you'll have a caring administrator who will attend and help wherever needed till the job is done. It may be difficult getting your administrator to that first party, but once you do, he'll probably want to attend them all. It's a good chance for families to get to know him personally, and they seem to enjoy that. And your administrator can take the bows because he has made the party possible. Of course, he'll probably give the credit back to you for all the hard work you have done in planning and carrying it out. But that's okay. You deserve it. It's a lot of work, true, but the next day when residents are still talking about the fun party, you'll know for sure that all your efforts were not in vain.

CHAPTER 8

Coming Forward
by Looking Back

Many activity directors spend countless hours trying to keep their administrators and state inspectors happy by involving residents in current events groups, and they become more frustrated by the moment. Some residents enjoy current events, but many just can't relate to the present like the past. This fast-paced world is so unlike the one in which they have spent most of their productive lives. Yet part of your job is to keep them orientated to the world around them and to keep them functioning at their maximum potential. So what's an activity director to do?

The answer is simple: Forget the present--for the moment--and go back into their world with them. Once there, bring them back to the present by comparing yesterday with today. To begin an active reminiscence group, you'll need information about their world in order to get residents not merely *listening* to what's happening today, but actively *talking* about their past lives. Let's explore some successful *old-days* subjects.

The first time you saw an automobile

- Do you remember the first time you saw an automobile?
- What did it look like?
- How did it sound?
- Did you ride in it?
- What did the horn sound like?
- What were acetylene light?
- Did they blink when you went up a hill? Why?
- What color was the car?
- Did it have a top on it?
- What size tires were on it?
- Were they like today's tires, or were they hard rubber?
- How much did those early cars cost?
- What kind was your first car?
- When did you buy it?

Driving in the old days

- What was the speed limit? Remember it being 10 mph?
- Remember when, in town, it was just 8 mph?
- Did you need a driver's license when you first drove?
- Did you need a car license plate?
- What kind of plate was it?
- Was it painted on the side of the car?
- Was it a little tag that hung inside the car?
- Were plates standard or were they ever homemade?
- How much did a license plate cost?
- Do you remember the first coast-to-coast highway *(1927)*
- What was the speed limit on that highway? *(40 mph)*
- Was gasoline ever limited?
- How much did gasoline cost?
- Tell me about your first car.

- Did you have any flat tires?
- Did flat tires happen often?

The old telephone
- What was your telephone number long ago?
- Was it two long rings and a short one?
- What did your telephone look like?
- Did it have a crank on the side?
- How did you call a neighbor?
- Who was *Central?*
- Did the phone ring in your house when it wasn't for you?
- Did you ever eavesdrop?
- Did the operator ever give a general ring?
- Did she tell you what movie would be playing?
- Did she pass messages like the ending of the war?

Needles and pins
- Did you ever sew?
- Did you have a machine? What kind?
- What fabric did you use? *percale? gingham? calico?*
- Did you ever sew from feed sacks?
- How did you bleach the feed sacks?
- Was there any permanent press fabric?
- Did clothes fade?

Shopping at home
- Remember the Raleigh Man?
- How about the Fuller Brush man?
- What did he sell?
- Was it brooms, spices, food coloring?
- Did many peddlers come by?

Radio days

- Did you have a radio when you were young?
- What did it look like?
- Did you ever make a receiver with an oatmeal box?
- Remember the one-tube set?
- What were some of the old programs?
- Who were the sponsors of those programs?
- How many channels could you get?
- Who was the *Arkansas Wood Chopper?*
- Who was *Lady Dickens?*
- Remember *Lullabelle and Scotty?*

Electricity

- Remember having your house first wired for electricity?
- How much did it cost? *($13)*
- What did that wiring consist of?
- Was it just a socket and wire hanging from the ceiling?
- Did you ever unscrew the bulb and carry it to the next room?
- What kind of lamps did you use before electricity?
- Were people ever afraid of electricity in their homes?
- What were the first electric appliances you got?

The Great Depression

- Do you remember the Great Depression?
- Tell me about it.
- What started it?
- Do you remember the stock market crash of 1929?
- Did you lose any money from a closed bank?
- Did you ever see a soup line?
- Did farmers manage better than city people?
- What happened to the price of crops?
- Why were animals slaughtered and milk dumped?

- What was the WPA? *(Works Projects Administration)*
- What did they do?
- Did you ever work for it?
- What President started it? *(Franklin Roosevelt)*
- What was the CCC? *(Civilian Conservation Corps)*
- What was the PWA? *(Public Works Administration*
- What was the Hoover House? *(outhouse)*

Big bands
- Remember the city bands?
- Did your town have one?
- Remember 4th of July band concerts?
- What was swing music?
- Who were Guy Lombardo? Benny Goodman? Harry James?
- Did you ever hear them play?
- What was *cutting the rug?*
- Remember Duke Ellington?
- Remember *It's a Sin To Tell a Lie?*
- Remember *Alexander's Ragtime Band?*
- What other songs do you remember?

The box social
- What is a box social?
- Did you ever go to one?
- Why did you decorate a shoe box?
- What went inside that box?
- What happened to the box?
- Did you ever get a girl or guy you didn't like?
- Where were the box socials held?
- How much money was raised on the boxes?
- What was it used for?

Street cars

- Did you ever ride a street car?
- Were they noisy?
- How much did it cost?
- What did it smell like?
- What kind of seats were in it?
- Who drove it?
- Where did it take you?
- Did you travel to ball games on it?
- Did it ever take you on a date?
- Did it ever slide down a hill on a winter day?
- Were there different cars for winter and summer?

Threshing days

- Did you ever work in a threshing ring?
- Did every man have a special job?
- What were some of those jobs?
- Where did you go for lunch?
- What were you served?
- What was the threshing machine like?
- What was it like to farm with horses?

Making do

- Did you ever have to work hard to make ends meet?
- Did your shoe soles ever wear out?
- How did you fix them?
- What happened to old coats?
- Did you ever clean them with gasoline?
- How did you save eggs to last all winter?
- What was *waterglass?*
- What happened when you got holes in your socks?
- How many dresses or pants did you have for school?

Hospitals

- Did you ever go to a hospital?
- Did you know someone who did?
- How much did it cost in the Twenties?
- What was your room like?
- Who took care of you there?
- Why did you have to go?
- Did people think hospitals were a place to die?

Preserving summer's bounty

- How did you cold pack?
- How did you keep carrots and apples for the winter?
- Some had root cellars. What if you didn't?
- Did you ever dry food?
- What was sunshine jam?
- How did you preserve rabbit?
- How was apple butter made?
- What about cider? sauerkraut?
- Did you ever hunt wild asparagus or strawberries along the railroad tracks?
- Do you remember the old *Presto* steam canner?
- Did you ever can outside with the wash boiler?

Old-time barber shops

- Where did you get your hair cut?
- Did women ever come to the shop for a cut?
- What kind of a cut did they get?
- Remember the Egyptian bob? shingle bob?
- Was there a shoe-shine boy at your shop?
- How much did a cut cost?
- Remember the straight razor?
- What is *Bay Rum?*

- What does it smell like?
- Did your barbers ever do a little singing?
- What magazines did you read there?
- What color was the striped pole outside the shop?

The old kitchen stove
- Remember the old kitchen stove?
- What did it look like?
- What was the brand name of it?
- Did it have a temperature-controlled oven?
- How did you know when cakes were done?
- What were warming ovens?
- How did you heat the stove?
- Where was the wood box kept? the coal bucket?
- Did you have a 20 gallon reservoir in the stove?
- Did you ever dress for school in front of it?
- Did you ever empty the ashes?
- What was blacking the old stove?
- Why did that have to be done?

Barn dances
- Did you ever go to a barn dance?
- What were they like?
- What did the people sit on?
- Where did the caller stand?
- What were the calls?
- What were some of the popular songs?
- How many squares of dancers were there?
- Did you have refreshments?
- How did you find out about the dances?
- Were they ever held in the hay mow?
- What kind of instruments were played?

Housekeeping

- Was the homemaker's work week organized?
- What did you do on each day of the week?
- What did you use to polish furniture?
- How was wallpaper cleaned?
- Did you make a substance with cornmeal, cook it and rub it on the walls like an eraser?
- What did you iron with?
- What was a fluting iron?
- What were the washboards made of?
- What was used to scrub the floor? the outhouse?
- How were clean curtains dried to keep from shrinking?

Shirley Temple

- Who was Shirley Temple?
- When was she popular?
- Did she ever make a movie?
- What were some of them?
- What about Shirley Temple did mothers try to copy?
- Why did they like her curls?
- Was there ever a doll made to look like her?
- Did you ever see or buy one?

Summary

As you see, any subject from days gone by can be used to draw up a set of questions. Your residents will love it. Plan a set time to have your group so residents can look forward to it. You might serve coffee and treats. This gets them there, and the discussion keeps them there. As leader of the group, it sometimes pays to *play dumb* even if you know the answers so residents can tell you something they think you don't know. This makes them feel worthwhile and proud that they are able to teach you something, since you're always teaching them things. As you reminisce with your residents about the past, you can use that past to draw them gradually back to the present. Talk about how things have changed. By doing this, you can satisfy the need for current events while actively involving residents in discussion that is close to their hearts.

A reminiscence group is valuable because even though you have a regularly-scheduled one, it can always be used again as a fill-in on those unpleasant occasions when your planned entertainment doesn't show up. Guests can be invited to your reminiscence group. You might invite residents from another facility or a senior citizen's group. Even one or two guest--sometimes just family members--can add new life and a new dimension to your group. This activity will quickly win your residents' hearts.

(For more such questions, see author's book, Remembering the Good Old Days, page 166)

CHAPTER 9

Ideas Unlimited

Running out of ideas? Sometimes an activity director finds herself in a rut. It seems she's done about every activity imaginable, and she doesn't know where to turn next. Here's a collection of tried and true ideas that may help.

Farm day

Many residents come from farm backgrounds. Hold a special day to honor them, but let all residents attend. Farmers might be honored by allowing them to sit in a certain area or by having special name tags, perhaps with an animal picture on them. If you or your volunteers are the type who are comfortable doing so, dress in bib overalls for the occasion. Have residents dress in farm clothes, even if it's just red handkerchiefs tied around their necks. Borrow some bales of hay to give a barn-like effect. Have a farmer bring in a piglet or a lamb. Maybe a farm implement company would bring a tractor to your facility for residents to go outside and inspect. They will no doubt be amazed at how tractors have changed since they farmed.

You might have a milking contest using rubber gloves filled with water that have a hole punched in the tip of a finger and let two resident compete against one another at *milking.* It will be necessary for someone to hold the gloves while residents milk them. Farm Day can be greatly expanded upon. Just let your imagination run free.

Safari day

First, visit your local travel bureau, and try to get some posters referring to Africa. Short of this, use large animal posters and pictures of wild animals cut from *National Geographic* or a sportsman or hunter-type magazine. Serve a special luncheon of monkey salad, rhino soup, alligator buns, tiger pie and a cake shaped like a lion. (This can be made from a round cake with cupcakes placed around it for the mane.) Use place mats with animal pictures on them. Serve animal cookies. Perhaps you have a local zoo or park that would bring a wild baby animal to visit. You may want to have a wild game hunt. This is done by placing the animal pictures you cut from the magazines all over one wall. Use toy dart guns with rubber suction-type darts, and have residents shoot the animals with them. It works best having not more than two shooting at once. Someone might choose to dress as Tarzan and Jane.

Funny day queen contest

Select a lady resident with a great sense of humor for your *funny day queen.* Make her a crown from a band of construction paper with glued on articles like plastic silverware, a scratcher, a big flower or any odds and ends that would bring a laugh. For a queen contest, there must be a bathing suit competition. Have your queen model a big tank top and baggy shorts. Let the queen's scepter be an upside down plunger with curled wrapping string flowing from the handle and a flower in the top. Present her with a bouquet.

This can be a cabbage leaf filled with green peppers, carrots, an apple and a flower. When the queen walks or wheels down the aisle, play an inappropriate song like *Ain't Nothing But a Hound Dog* or *London Bridges*. This activity gives residents a chance to really laugh out loud, something they don't always get a chance to do. They'll love it.

Hatch chicks

This is an activity that captivates residents. It's sometimes hard to get them to bed at night if it looks like an egg is about to hatch. You can sometimes borrow an incubator through a university's poultry department or possibly through a chicken hatchery, or you can make your own. Get a good-sized cardboard box. Measure the size of the bottom, and go to a hardware store and buy a piece of chicken wire made up of about one-fourth inch squares. Have them cut you a piece of it two inches larger all around than the box bottom. With pliers and a straight edge, bend this wire down two inches on all four sides to create a box-like effect. Slip this in the bottom of your box as a raised floor for the eggs to rest on, and for the chickens to walk on when they hatch. Beneath it is your box floor lined with aluminum foil. Now locate a large, old picture frame with glass about the size of the front of the box when lying on its side. This acts as a viewing window for residents to watch the hatching. You will need to cut out a square in the front of the box, the size of the picture glass, but try to keep it from having too many air leaks. A small dish of water must be kept in the incubator at all times for humidity which the eggs require to hatch. You will also need to keep a thermometer in the box that should remain between 98 and 101 degrees. To get this temperature, you will need a drop cord with a light bulb in a wire casing attached to hang in the box and remain on at all times. To avoid being a fire hazard, you will have to be very careful how you hang it and continue to check it regularly. You may even want to line the areas near where it hangs with aluminum foil. The light has to be hung high enough that the chicks will not get burnt on it. You'll have to experiment with various size light bulbs till you find the one that will hold your temperature steady. With that accomplished, now you will need to find fertile eggs. Check with a poultry house or a farmer who raises chickens. It takes about three weeks for them to hatch. I've found it more enjoyable for the residents if I let the farmer incubate the eggs the first two weeks and carefully move them from the farm to my facility the last week in a styrofoam cooler. This way the wait isn't so long for the residents.

Don't get too anxious when you see the first crack. Sometimes they come quickly, but most often, it is some time from the first crack to the actual hatching. Resist the urge to help the chicks out of the egg. The chicks survive well for a couple of days in the incubator with the unhatched eggs. Be sure to keep a saucer of water in it for them to drink, and have some chick feed on hand. It is said they don't need it for a day or so, but it doesn't hurt to have it in the incubator. One word of caution: When you take the chicks out of the incubator, air conditioning in a facility is often too cold for them. You may need to keep them covered and possibly even keep a light for heat in the new box in which you put them. This does not have to be kept at 100 degrees though. In a few days, residents can hold them. Ducks can be hatched the same way and seem much heartier, though they are slightly more messy. Yet they are bigger, and residents can more easily see and handle them. They will follow you, just like they would a mother duck, down the hall while you make rounds. They can be kept for two or three weeks in the facility before going back to the farm. Residents enjoy watching the ducks swim in a water-filled big plastic container in the center of the activity room. Generally, some staff members will want to keep the ducks, but unless they live in the country and can actually care for them, it's best to return them to the farmer who provided the eggs. This activity has always proved a hit with residents.

Make apple head dolls

This project can take several activity sessions. Give an apple to each resident, and let those who are able to handle a knife carve their own. Have them peel it, or peel it for them. Be sure to leave the stems on for hanging to dry in a window when cut. Allow them to cut slits for eyes and cheeks and for what will later become wrinkles. Drying takes at least a couple of weeks. As the apples shrink, the features become more pronounced. When the heads are dry, form the bodies by bending wire to make stick-type people with arms and legs and necks that attach to the head. This wire body is then wrapped with cotton to put *meat on the bones*. Next clothes are made. Make overalls for the men dolls and long granny dresses for the women dolls to cover their roughly-made bodies. Since these dolls are so small, you or volunteers will probably have to sew the clothes. Pieces of wire can be formed to make miniature glasses. This is a project that works best with more specific directions. Go to your library and get a book on making apple head dolls. The children's section is a good place to find these and other books on craft projects written simply; you won't need to spend a lot of time learning an involved craft in a more complicated book.

Hold a mini-olympics

This is an activity that can be done in an hour's time. You might have easy competitions such as shot-put where cotton balls are thrown and the distance measured. Hold a fifty-yard dash by having residents sew fifty stitches with yarn on burlap and see who finishes first. Have a javelin throw with residents tossing soda straws. Have each one smile real big. Get your tape measure, and find out who has the longest *sitting broad grin*. You might have a penny-pitch with residents throwing pennies in egg cartons. This has been a successful activity among nursing home residents.

Magazine scavenger hunt

Before beginning, go through a big stack of magazines, and make a list of items in them for the scavenger hunt. This list might consist of such things as: a lady in a green dress, a tiger, a blue shoe, a pie, a man working, and a small dog. Select about thirty items. Divide residents into two or more teams. Have maybe seven residents on each team though the number is not important. Gather teams around tables. Give them each a stack of magazines. It's helpful to have someone to assist each team because residents usually can't keep track of what they've found and what they haven't. But one activity director can fairly easily handle this one alone if necessary. When residents find the picture of the specificized item, have them tear it out and put it in a pile. At mid-point, switch the stacks of magazines so each team has a different supply and a fair chance of finding the items on their list. The first team to find all the items is the winner. You might reward them with a selection from the bingo prizes. Be sure to give a consolation prize such as candy or cookies to all who take part.

Paper potluck

Everyone enjoys a potluck dinner. Residents, though, often don't have the opportunity to make choices about what they will eat. If your dietitian would want to take part, definitely invite her to this one. Before the activity, cut colorful, attractively served food pictures from magazines. Include meats, fruits, vegetables, bread, salads and desserts. Arrange meats on one serving tray, breads another, desserts another and so on. Give each resident a paper plate. Then let them select, as if this were a real potluck supper, what they would like to eat. It's surprising. They spend as much time selecting paper foods as they would the real thing. The dietitian takes note of the foods they select. She can talk a little about nutrition to the residents. The paper potluck also serves to tell her what foods residents enjoy eating and gives her new ideas for meal planning. This is an easy activity for which to plan, and residents seem to enjoy it.

Put on your old gray bonnet

A proper lady in our residents' day never left the house without her hat. Here's her chance to bring back those days by making her own beautiful bonnet. This is good to do during the Easter season but can be done anytime. Get out all your odds-and-ends craft supplies and funeral ribbons. Include artificial flowers, glitter, beads, bows, etc. Don't forget glue and a stapler. Give each lady (sometimes men like to make them, too, for their favorite ladies) a paper plate as the base of her hat. Help her run a funeral ribbon across the top and down through cut slits on the plate so she can tie it under her chin when finished. Now allow residents to use their imagination and create lovely bonnets. When they are finished, have them all model their creations, and take their picture so they'll remember the event for a long time.

Hats off to the workers

An activity director wears many hats. So do other workers. Hats are worn for fun, too. Collect as many as you can find: mailman, fast-food worker, painter, sock cap, ladies hats from past and present, football helmet, baseball cap, derby, nurses cap and sailor hat. Borrow from friends and staff, your kids and your neighbors. You might even want to hit the Goodwill store. Spend an hour with residents letting them model the hats and tell you when each would be appropriately worn. Be sure to provide mirrors for them to admire themselves.

Gone fishing

More alert residents can sometimes go on a fishing trip outside the facility which is wonderful. What about the confused or handicapped though? Why not have an indoor fishing contest? Go through sports magazines and cut out all the pictures of fish you can find--big ones and little ones. Put Scotch tape near each fish's mouth for strength and run a paper clip through it. Next take four big cardboard boxes and draw waves on the outside of the boxes with blue and green markers. Push these boxes together to form one big square which is the lake. Place your fish in the bottom of the boxes. Position wheel chairs around the *lake* and hand each resident a fishing pole. These can be cane poles or long dowel rods or sticks with strings attached. Attach a magnet on the end of each line to attract the paper clip in the fish's mouth. Have residents fish by moving their poles around till they snag a fish. Give prizes for the most fish and the biggest one.

Make a mural

Make a community mural. Newspapers will usually give you *roll ends* of unprinted newspaper. These are good size rolls that can be used for many purposes. Use this or the back side of a roll of wallpaper. Gather residents around tables that have been pushed together, and give them markers, crayons or paint brushes and paint, and ask them to create something. You might suggest their picture be of their first school, or the home of their childhood. It might be a special tree that they swung from or climbed in. They might want to draw the park where they played as children or a special flower garden they planted. Be sure to have residents sign their pictures on the mural. If they are unable, sign it for them. When the mural is finished, proudly display it on a long wall in your facility.

Something's cooking

Cooking requires a lot from the activity director, but it has big rewards for residents who have spent a good part of their lives in the kitchen. Making donuts is always a successful activity. Simply buy refrigerated biscuits in the can at the grocery store. Let residents place these on cookie sheets. Then using a small object such as a salt-shaker top, cut a hole out of the center of each biscuit. Beforehand, heat grease in a slow cooker or deep fryer. It's extremely important to watch this carefully so residents do not get too close or get burned. When the donuts are cut, drop them in hot grease and let them cook about two minutes. If it takes less time, they will be doughy in the middle. If cooked too long, they will be greasy. Only the activity director or a reliable volunteer should handle the actual frying part. When the donuts are cooked, let residents roll them in cinnamon and sugar or powdered sugar. Often diabetics are allowed one without sugar though each patient's diet has to be individually evaluated. If you need to make money for your department, here's an opportunity. When the sweet aroma of donuts frying spreads throughout the facility, everyone will be looking for a sample. You might charge a dime a piece.

Photo sharing

Have all residents bring their photo album or any pictures they have, and let residents spend an hour looking at each other's pictures and laughing about how they looked when they were young.

Photo contest

Contact families and ask them to bring in the wedding pictures of your residents. Display these on a bulletin board and have staff, families and visitors put their guess about who everyone is in a specially provided box. This can also be done with baby pictures.

Show and tell

Have each resident bring something from his room that has special meaning to him. When everyone is gathered together, let each one tell about his item and its significance.

Looking up

Have someone who has mastered stilts come in and visit residents and walk about the facility towering over everyone. In the same manner, you might invite someone who owns a motorcycle to visit and let residents go outside to look it over.

The fire department might bring an engine down for residents to see, and they might even demonstrate the siren for them. The police department, in some towns, will bring a police car or police dog.

No prohibition here

If there are no rules or regulations barring it at your facility, have your residents make wine one afternoon. It only takes a glass gallon bottle with a small neck, two twelve-ounce cans of frozen grape juice, four cups of sugar, and about a tablespoon of yeast. Mix this all in the gallon jug. Next, fill the jug with water. Stir, and then stretch the mouth of a large round balloon over the top of the jug. Poke a hole in the end of the balloon with a needle. The balloon will soon begin to rise as the yeast works and will later go down some as the wine nears completion. Set this jar aside for two weeks at which time it should be done. Serve it sparingly though it's not that potent. On the day residents make the wine, try to involve them in a discussion about prohibition. Ask if any of them, or people they knew, made their own beer in those days when it was illegal to buy it. Get them talking also about the *speakeasies* of the Twenties and Thirties.

Color me beautiful

Ladies never outgrow the desire to look attractive. Invite someone in who does the color analysis program where they determine what color looks best on individuals. They will usually do make-up as well, on a few residents. Also a seller of cosmetics might be persuaded to come in and make-up some residents or at least share about some of their products. Another similar activity is to have a school class of girls (about 8th grade) come in and make female residents look pretty. They can paint fingernails, use curling irons on their hair and experiment with make-up on willing residents.

A visit to the photographer

Announce to residents that one special afternoon will be picture-taking day. Encourage them to dress nice. This usually doesn't take any encouragement. They love to have their pictures taken and automatically spruce up a bit. That's part of the fun of the activity. Choose a plain wall for an uncluttered background, and one by one, snap their pictures. Don't forget to visit the room-bound patients; take their picture in their room. When they are developed, hang them all up on a big bulletin board with letters spelling out, "Meet Our Family." It's hard for anyone visiting the facility to avoid stopping and viewing these pictures.

Mock wedding

Begin to involve residents a week or two before the actual wedding. It will quickly be the talk of the facility. Write an interesting press release, and send it to all the newspapers and television stations in your area. You might even want to invite your radio station to do some *on the spot* reporting. Choose a bride, groom, best man, bridesmaids, mother of the bride, father of the bride, judge or preacher and any others you want to include. Plan the outfits they will wear. This is to be a very funny affair. The bride may wear a white nightgown for a dress, and a bed sheet pulled up with a big flower at the top for a veil. The groom can wear any kind of suit. The mother of the bride can wear an old fur about her shoulders, and the father of the bride will need a shotgun (a toy one is fine). Try to find some type of fancy dresses for the bridesmaids. Big straw hats with flowers on them are nice, too. It's good to have a corsage (any funny flower will do--even those made from tissues) for all the wedding party. Guests can be given one if you have enough. For the aisle runner, unwind a roll of red and white checked table covering or something equally as ridiculous. Even though this is fun and residents laugh a lot, they still take their parts very seriously. Write a silly ceremony. Record the wedding march and a recessional, and use them at the proper time to put everyone in the mood. Have a funny wedding cake available. This can be just two round cakes purchased at a supermarket and stacked on top of each other. Put Snoopy or a Mickey Mouse replica or something similar on top. After the ceremony, be sure to have the groom kiss his bride. Take lots of pictures, and even better, make a video so the wedding can be enjoyed again and again. Serve the cake and enjoy the fun.

Before you write your ceremony, you must know your residents in order to write a silly ceremony. Take their personalities into account. It's important to choose residents who have a good sense of humor, who can laugh at themselves and have a good time. This particular ceremony was written for two residents, by residents. The lady, on the surfaces was rough and even unkind to those about her, but inside she had a wonderful heart. She could joke about her rough personality and often did. The man in this ceremony was a short, little, fun-loving man from the hills of Kentucky who would tease his *bride* right back if she tried to get the best of him. That's why this ceremony reads as it does.

MAKE-BELIEVE CEREMONY

"We are joined here together in the presence of these witnesses to join this couple in *HOKEY MACARONI.* This good old-fashioned, make-believe "weeding" will join Lilly *Fiesty* Jones and Sammie *Tiger* Hathaway."

"Sammie, will you take this gentle-natured woman to be your make-believe madam to have and to hold till 3:00 do you part?"
"I'll consider it."
"Lilly, will you take this rattlesnake lover boy to be your unlawfully-loaded doom till 3:00 do you part?"
"I might as well."
"With this ring, we'll probably turn red, but...
...by the authority vested in me as comedian of this ABC Nursing Home, I now pronounce you...
man and strife!
You may kiss your bride."
and the bride added...
"May this macaroni ceremony produce many little spaghetti(s)!"

Nursing home olympics

Sometimes it's fun to involve your residents with residents of other facilities. If you are a good organizer, and you probably are or you wouldn't be an activity director, why not start an annual nursing home olympics in your district? Begin by calling all the other facilities within a twenty-mile radius of yours, and ask them if they'd like to take part. When you have a group interested, get three or four A.D.'s to help you. Secure a place such as a school gym in which to hold the olympics. Next plan the events. Some tried and true ones are:

- wheel chair
- wheelchair obstacle course
- walking race
- free-throw contest
- bucket basketball
- bean bag toss
- flying saucers (paper plates sailed through hula hoops)
- bean bags in clown mouth
- dance contest (final event)

Locate someone to be an emcee. A radio announcer is good or a well-known community figure. See if your mayor or state representative will offer a brief introduction. Call a local dance studio, and see if some of their dancers will act as judges for your dance contest. Order helium to fill balloons that will be given to all residents who come. Get a copy of the *National Anthem* on tape to be played at the opening of your olympics. Get a kitchen band or any band to play between events. After the *National Anthem* and the word from the politician, begin the event with a parade of all residents marching or wheeling around the gym to the tune of *When the Saints Go Marching In*. Have residents from each facility carry a banner with their facility's name on it.

All facilities who come should bring volunteers to help their residents. Total number of residents participating will probably be over a hundred. If you hold the event in a school, try to get a whole class of 8th graders (or any class) to assist wherever needed. They can push wheelchair residents up to compete in competitions, and they can help at the events. They can run the registration table, pass out awards, run errands and serve refreshments.

Refreshments can be simply popcorn and orange drink (purchased from McDonald's), or donated soda pop. Popcorn can all be popped beforehand and brought in a huge plastic bag. Have each home participating pay an entrance fee of twenty to twenty-five dollars which will pay for printed ribbons, little plastic trophies, helium, name tags and refreshments. Facilities may bring any number of residents---if you can accommodate them. Residents may pick and choose the events in which they want to compete. Everyone gets a participation ribbon just for coming. Invite the media and the public. Have someone video-tape it. This is a highly successful event, but it takes a motivated leader and lots of planning. The rewards for everyone, though, are tremendous--and that makes all the effort wonderfully worthwhile.

Summary

Activity ideas are everywhere. Take any given activity you see going on around you, and ask yourself: "How could I adapt this activity for my residents?"

Another excellent source of activity ideas come from the *Activity Director Guide* (see page 161). A good rule of thumb is to try holding at least one *new* activity each month. This is one way to keep your program alive, active and diversified--and that's just what a professional activity director seeks to do.

CHAPTER *10*

Outings for Residents

Even though an activity director has a very diverse and active program, there are still times when it benefits both her and her residents to get them out into the community. Let's examine some ideas that have in the past proven successful with activity directors.

Back to school

Did any of your residents attend the local high school? Does that school still have the yearbooks available from the years your residents attended? If so, you have the makings, not only for a successful outing, but a sure story for the press. Most schools that publish yearbooks keep a copy of all issues in their yearbook room. Call the school and ask for the yearbook advisor. Introduce yourself, and tell her you have some former students at your facility who graduated in the class of 1929 or whenever. Tell her you would like to bring them to school to meet with her class, and if possible, see the yearbooks with their pictures in them. She will probably be delighted to help you. The principal, himself, might even meet you at the front door and escort you. Residents will delight in being in old familiar surroundings and seeing how differently things are done in school today. School kids seem to be on their best behavior when the seniors come, and really enjoy their visit. And the T.V. and newspaper reporters like it because it is something different.

Grammar school

The fact that residents generally like kids, and that some residents have only an eighth grade education makes visiting a grammar school a worthwhile activity. Think ahead about what you'd like to do on your visit. A share time where residents tell of their school days and the children ask questions is always interesting. Many residents remain good spellers so a spelling bee is fun as is as reviewing basic mathematic tables or states and capitals. They might sing some of the old songs that both generations know. Drawing, painting or coloring are fun, as are playing old-time games like *twenty questions* or *I spy*. Taking a gift made by residents would be a nice gesture.

The antique store

Many activity directors enjoy taking their residents to a mall. A new twist is to visit an antique store. Even better than just an antique store is one made to resemble an old-time store with glass-cased wooden counters, old barrels, and floor-to-ceiling wooden shelves. What seems antique to us was once a necessity for them. They'll enjoy the old cooking stove, the sad irons, sewing machines, kitchen utensils, furniture, farm tools and toys of their childhood. This brings back many good memories. If you take notes of the things and products there, you will have the makings of a lively reminiscence session with your residents the next morning.

Be a parade

In your residents day, parades were big entertainment. Let them make up their own parade. This is good around Memorial Day or the Fourth of July. If your facility is located near a downtown or shopping area, this activity works well. If not, you might consider loading up residents and their wheel chairs, and taking them downtown. It's wise to check with your local police department to let them know you'll be pushing residents in a given area.

Invite school kids (junior high or high school works well) to be a part of your parade. Have them come to your facility and help decorate residents' wheel chairs with crepe paper and helium balloons. Don't forget signs on wheel chairs identifying your facility. When you are ready to go, assign each child a resident to push during the parade. Needless to say, this activity attracts much attention. I've noticed that even though cars had to wait through three light changes while our parade of residents were pushed across the streets, they didn't seem to mind too much but rather enjoyed the parade. A trip around the downtown square is a highlight of the trip for residents.

It's wise to have all residents in wheel chairs, even if they are able to walk. Not only do they become tired, but there could be danger if they wrongly walked out into a street. It's important that all possible precautions are taken for the residents' safety. This also is a sure to bring good press coverage to your facility.

A ride about town

Sometimes the worlds of our residents become very small. They forget just what their town looks like. If your facility is located in the city, your local bus company may allow one of their buses to come to your facility and take residents on a regular bus route tour through the city. Though this may sound like a small activity, for the residents, it may be one of the high points of their year as they view businesses, schools, churches and neighborhoods they haven't seen for ages.

Fishing trip

This activity takes some planning, but it is worth the effort. There's something about the open air, a picnic, and a flowing river that allows residents to forget, for a time, that they live in nursing home. The fishing spot must be selected carefully so you'll have easy access for your residents to fish. A private lake where you pay to fish may be your wisest choice unless you can find a level area big enough for everyone where you can get wheelchairs close enough to the water without danger. You will also need a place with a picnic table. An adequate number of volunteers are necessary. One per patient is not too many. If possible, bring an aide or two along to help residents to the rest room and to assist with other personal needs. Try to get some fishermen to go along to put worms on hooks and take fish off. This will free you to oversee the outing. Always be alert for a resident needing assistance. Maybe your administrator would like to go along. If so, it is good for everyone. Residents enjoy a chance to talk with him on an informal basis. He can be a great help to you in meeting the many demands of a fishing trip. He can also get a feel for all you go through on an outing with residents.

Have your kitchen pack a picnic lunch made as simple as possible to serve. Sandwiches, cookies, bananas and other hand foods are easiest. Inexpensive cane poles can sometimes be purchased at sporting goods stores. They may give you a discount if you tell them what the poles will be used for. Short of this, borrow fishing poles. The fishing trip does not need to be an all-day affair. Two or three hours is about all many residents can comfortably take. Something that makes the trip a little more lively is to have someone play a guitar or banjo and sing a little for residents after lunch. This isn't necessary, but it adds an extra touch.

One of my residents got so wound up when the banjo music started that he began to dance. Unfortunately the faster he went, the looser his pants became till they finally fell down around his ankles. He and the other residents laughed about that for months.

You're never too old for baseball

Take Me Out to the Ball Game was a favorite song in residents' day. Baseball used to be more popular than it is today. Why not bring back those good memories by taking them to a ball game? For time and convenience sake, it's easier to take them to a children's ball game rather than a professional one. These are usually held on fields without many fences, thus you are free to push wheelchairs close to the field. You can leave, then, whenever you need, without much commotion.

Summary

These are just a few ideas for outings. There are many more-- going out for a pizza, visiting an ice cream parlor or visiting the park. Residents may enjoy a tour of the police station, fire station, library, animal shelter or a local zoo. Even a few outings each year will break the monotony, for residents, of a life spent mostly indoors. It will also let them know that they are still a vital part of their community.

CHAPTER *11*

Word Games:
Wonderful for Emergencies

You have your residents all gathered together and they are beginning to get restless. Your entertainment was due fifteen minutes ago. You wait ten more minutes and realize they are not going to show. You don't want to disappoint your residents, but you don't have anything else planned. What are you going to do?

It's frustrating when this happens, but a professional activity director doesn't despair. Unless she has a talent where she can open the piano and begin to play, the next best thing is to have a collection of word games on hand that can be pulled out on a moment's notice.

Word games, though, are not just to use in case of *no shows.* If you want to keep your residents mentally alert, try using these games daily while they are waiting for lunch to be served. They can also be used as entertainment for various parties. Collect them, and make yourself a book using a loose-leaf binder. Where do you get word games? Everywhere--in the newspaper, from your children's school papers, in magazines, at wedding and baby showers, or you can make them up yourself. Just take any subject, and begin to ask yourself questions about it. Make the questions simple enough for residents to know the answers, but not so simple as to bore them. Let's take a look at some word games that you might want to use.

Times and seasons

1) Name the months of the year. *Jan. Feb. Mar.*
2) What year was America discovered? *1492*
3) How many days in a year? *365* In leap year? *366*
4) What is the shortest month? *February*
5) How many hours are there in a day? *24*
6) How many weeks in a year? *52*
7) How many months in a year? *12*
8) Name as many holidays as you can. *New Years, Valentine's Day, St. Pat's Day, Easter, Mother's Day, Memorial Day, Father's Day, July 4th, Labor Day, Halloween, Thanksgiving, Christmas, Hanukkah*
9) When does spring start? *March 21*
10) Who was the first President? *George Washington*
11) Who is President now?
12) Name the four seasons? *summer, winter, spring, fall*
13) Name as many kinds of trees as you can. *oak, maple, pine, birch, fruit, evergreen*
14) Name four oceans. *Atlantic, Pacific, Indian, Arctic*
15) What continent do we live on? *North American*
16) Name the continents. *North America, South America, Europe, Asia, Africa, Australia, Antarctica*
17) How many rivers can you name? *Mississippi, Hudson, Nile, Ohio, Wabash*
18) When do you plant potatoes? *Good Friday*

Simple sports quiz

1) What do you call it when you score in football? *touchdown*
2) How many points does one get for a basket in basketball? *2*
3) How many points does one get for a free throw? *1*
4) How many points are given for a touchdown in football? *6*
5) What do you call a score in bowling when you knock all the pins down? *strike*
6) What is it called when two tries are needed to knock them all down? *spare*
7) How many pins are there in all? *10*
8) Name some positions on a football team. *quarterback, fullback, halfback, lineman*
9) Name some positions on a basketball team. *center, forward, guard*
10) What sport do you play using a bat and a ball? *baseball*
11) How many men are there on a baseball team? *9*
12) Who was the "home-run king?" *Babe Ruth*
13) What game starts by jumping for a ball? *basketball*
14) What games starts with a throw of a ball? *baseball*
15) What game starts by the blow of a whistle? *football, soccer*
16) How many men are on a football team? *11*
17) Who was the famous coach of Notre Dame? *Knute Rockney*
18) What is the nickname for the Purdue team? *Boilermakers*
19) How do you score in basketball? *ball through a hoop*
20) How do you score in baseball? *get a run*

President quiz

1) Who was the first President of the U.S.? *George Washington*
2) What President taught himself to read? *Abraham Lincoln*
3) What man who later became President led the Rough Riders up San Juan hill? *Teddy Roosevelt*
4) What was Teddy Roosevelt's famous daughter's name? *Alice*

5) Do you remember anything unique about her? *She slid down the banisters in front of guests and sometimes carried garter snakes in her purse.*

6) Name two Presidents who were Indian fighters. *William Henry Harrison and Zachary Taylor*

7) What President died of pneumonia one month after his election as a result of not wearing a hat or coat during his inaugural address? *William Henry Harrison*

8) Who was the first President to wear long pants in the White House? *Thomas Jefferson*

9) Who was the last President to wear a beard? *Benjamin Harrison*

10) What President was called "Rough and Ready?" *Zachary Taylor*

11) Who is called the "father of our constitution"? *James Madison*

12) Who was the only President to be married in the White House? *Grover Cleveland*

13) Did Harry S. Truman always live in the White House as President? *No. From 1948-52 he lived across the street in Blair House while the White House was being remodeled.*

14) What President purchased the Louisiana Territory? *Thomas Jefferson*

15) Approximately how many rooms are in the White House? *100*

16) What are the three things required to be President?
1) must be a citizen of U.S.
2) must be at least 35 years old
3) must have been a resident of the U.S. for 14 years

Brief facts about Presidents

GEORGE WASHINGTON
- trained to work with figures from his youth
- spent much time camping in summers
- one of the richest citizen of the country

- was called the "Virginia patriot"
- lived at Mt. Vernon
- bullet once pierced his hat and coat
- occupation: surveyor, planter, soldier
- died at 70

THOMAS JEFFERSON
- believed in free schools and religious liberty and everyone's right to speak his mind
- read Greek and Latin
- studied law
- wrote the Declaration of Independence
- worked on inventions
- established our present money system of dollars and cents
- stood six foot six-inches tall

ANDREW JACKSON
- was a revolutionary soldier at age thirteen
- was a student of law

FRANKLIN D. ROOSEVELT
- stricken with infantile paralysis in 1921 and lost use of both legs
- as President-elect, an attempt was once made to assassinate him in Miami, Florida
- organized the "New Deal"
- re-elected in 1936 by largest popular vote ever at that time
- famous for saying, "Eleanor hates war, Falo hates war, and I hate war!"
- famous for saying, "The only thing we have to fear is fear itself."

HARRY S. TRUMAN

- took over presidency in 1945 when Roosevelt died of a massive cerebral hemorrhage
- authorized the first use of atomic bomb in warfare on cites of Hiroshima and Nagasaki

(Much more presidential trivia can be found in Marge Knoth's new book Newsletters Simplified! (see page 166).

New York quiz

1) Has anyone ever visited New York?
2) What do you remember about it?
3) When immigrants first came to the U.S., what Eastern city was usually their first one to settle in? *New York*
4) When the ship first arrived, what was the first stop for clearance? *Ellis Island*
5) New York is divided into sections. Can you name them? *Queens, Manhattan, Bronx, Staten Island, Brooklyn*
6) What building has been known as the tallest in New York? *Empire State* building
7) How many stories does it have? *102*
8) How many windows does it have? *6,500*
9) Are they ever washed? If so how often? *yes; two times a month*
10) How many people visit the Empire State building annually? *1.5 million*
11) What do you see when approaching New York Harbor? *Statue of Liberty*
12) Where did we get the Statue of Liberty? *gift from France*
13) What year did we receive it? *1884*
14) How tall is it? *150 feet high*
15) Do you remember it being massively repaired? *yes; in the 80's*
16) What else might you see in New York? *Macy's, Broadway plays, Times Square, Radio City*

17) How much does it cost to get a taxi cab license in New York? *(one-time fee) $60,000*

18) What ball teams has New York been famous for? *Brooklyn Dodgers, (now Los Angeles Dodgers) New York Yankees, New York Mets*

19) What percentage of New York people are of foreign birth? *50%*

20) Would you like to live in New York? Why?

States and capitals

This game works best with residents if you give them the capital and let them tell you the state.

Alabama: Montgomery

Alaska: Juneau

Arizona: Phoenix

Arkansas: Little Rock

California: Sacramento

Colorado: Denver

Connecticut: Hartford

Delaware: Dover

Florida: Tallahassee

Georgia: Atlanta

Hawaii: Honolulu

Idaho: Boise

Illinois: Springfield

Indiana: Indianapolis

Iowa: Des Moines

Kansas: Topeka

Kentucky: Frankfort

Louisiana: Baton Rouge

Maine: Augusta

Maryland: Annapolis

Massachusetts: Boston

Montana: Helena

Nebraska: Lincoln

Nevada: Carson City

New Hampshire: Concord

New Jersey: Trenton

New Mexico: Santa Fe

New York: Albany

North Carolina: Raleigh

North Dakota: Bismarck

Ohio: Columbus

Oklahoma: Oklahoma City

Oregon: Salem

Pennsylvania: Harrisburg

Rhode Island: Providence

South Carolina: Columbia

South Dakota: Pierre

Tennessee: Nashville

Texas: Austin

Utah: Salt Lake City

Vermont: Montpelier

Virginia: Richmond

Michigan: Lansing   Washington: Olympia
Minnesota: St. Paul   West Virginia: Charleston
Mississippi: Jackson   Wisconsin: Madison
Missouri: Jefferson City   Wyoming: Cheyenne

Famous inventors

WHO INVENTED THE FOLLOWING?

1) Cotton gin: *Eli Whitney*

2) Repeating rifle: *Oliver Winchester*

3) Machine gun: *Gatling*

4) Lightening rod: *Ben Franklin*

5) Radio: *Marconi*

6) Paper: *Chinese*

7) Victrola: *Thomas Edison*

8) Airplane: *Wright Brothers*

9) Penicillin: *Alexander Fleming*

10) Telephone: *Alexander Graham Bell*

11) Gun powder: *Chinese*

12) Light bulb: *Thomas Edison*

Measurement chart

WHAT ARTICLES MATCH THE SIZES BELOW?

1) 2 X 4: *board*

2) 9 1/2 short: *nylons*

3) 9 X 12: *rug or room*

4) 21 inch: *television*

5) 14 or 14 1/2: *shirt*

6) 8 X 10: *picture*

7) 81 X 108: *sheet*

8) 6 3/4: *hat*

9) 22" by 44": *towel*

Some laundry products
1) Wind blowing through the trees: *Breeze*
2) People yelling, screaming, shouting: *Cheer*
3) Put into motion: *Action*
4) Super, fantastic: (slang) *Fab*
5) When you achieve: *Gain*
6) Winter weather conditions: *Snowy*
7) Everything in the world: *All*
8) To steer a car: *Drive*

Old proverbs
1) He that goes barefoot must not plant: *thorns*
2) Other men eat to live while I: *live to eat*
3) As you make your bed, so must you: *lie in it*
4) Strike while the iron is: *hot*
5) Trouble runs off him like: *water on a duck's back*
6) Heaven helps those who: *help themselves*
7) Honesty is the best: *policy*
8) What's sauce for the goose is sauce for the: *gander*
9) Leave well enough: *alone*
10) It's never too late to: *learn*
11) No sooner said than: *done*
12) You can't teach an old dog: *new tricks*
13) Barking dogs never: *bite*
14) Early to bed and early to rise makes a man: *healthy, wealthy and wise*
15) Misery loves: *company*
16) Make hay while: *the sun shines*
17) Blood is thicker than: *water*
18) The big toad in: *a little puddle*
19) Absence makes the heart: *grow fonder*
20) April showers bring: *May flowers*
21) The early bird catches the: *worm*

22) Faint heart never won: *fair lady*
23) Never grieve over: *spilled milk*
24) A new broom: *sweeps clean*
25) When the cat's away: *the mice will play*

The name game

1) Name a beverage you put ice in.
2) Name something you'd put butter one.
3) Name a patriotic song.
4) Name a famous man called Jackie.
5) Name a tropical island.
6) Name a household appliance.
7) Name something you would keep in the refrigerator.
8) Name a face that appears on paper currency.
9) Name a holiday in February.
10) Name a fruit that has lots of seeds.
11) Name a word that rhymes with *hope.*
12) Name a very big breed of dog.
13) Name a berry.
14) Name a kind of pie.
15) Name a fruit you'd eat for breakfast.
16) Name a Southern food.
17) Name something that grows on a vine.
18) Name a President of the United States who wore a beard.
19) Name something a door-to-door salesman might sell.
20) Name a state where you might still find cowboys.
21) Name a job for a man who wears a white uniform.
22) Name a job for a woman who wears a white uniform.
23) Name a chewy candy.
24) Name a city in Canada.
25) Name an occupation where a man wears white coveralls.
26) Name a flower that grows in a window box.
27) Name something you'd put sugar on.

28) Name something that might take years to pay for.
29) Name a great actress.
30) Name a song with the word *blue* in the title.
31) Name a girl's nickname that is also a boy's name.
32) Name a bridge.
33) Name someone you might make an appointment to see.
34) Name an animal act you might see at the circus.
35) Name a flower that grows on a bush.
36) Name a famous flyer.
37) Name something that costs a dime.
38) Name someone who has received a lot of publicity.
39) Name something that makes crumbs when you eat it.
40) Name something a woman might forget to check on a car.
41) Name a man's occupation beginning with the letter "P".
42) Name a way a young boy might make money.
43) Name something you could cook on a camping trip.
44) Name a boy in a nursery rhyme.
45) Name a fish.
46) Name a hair color.
47) Name the household chore you do not mind doing.
48) Name a word that rhymes with *bunny*.
49) Name an unfriendly animal
50) Name a woman in history who was very beautiful.
51) Name a state with a very long name.
52) Name someone famous with the name William or Bill.
53) Name something kids drink for lunch.
54) Name a country that ends with the letters *land*.
55) Name a movie star whose last name begins with "G".
56) Name an occupation where you use a ladder.

Food fun

1) Hamburgers are as American as: *apple pie*
2) To earn a living is called to bring home the: *bacon*

3) Identical twins are as alike as: *two peas in a pod*
4) If you don't believe what someone is saying, you say that's a lot of: *baloney*
5) People with a lot of gray above their foreheads are said to have: *salt and pepper hair*
6) When fog becomes so thick you could slice it, you say it's as: *thick as pea soup*
7) When a person is embarrassed he turns red as a: *beet*
8) An eccentric person might be said to be as nutty as a: *fruitcake*
9) Easy money is called: *gravy*
10) Folding money is called: *lettuce*
11) A smart person knows his: *onions*
12) Something of little value might be said not to be worth: *a hill of beans*
13) If a prize fighter swings at you, you: *duck*
14) Someone who doesn't easily get upset or nervous might be said to be as cool as a: *cucumber*
15) Someone who is easily scared is called: *chicken*
16) If Cinderella wasn't home by midnight, her coach would turn into a: *pumpkin*
17) A crowded bus might pack riders in like: *sardines*
18) Adam and Eve sinned when they ate the: *apple*
19) A President once said "a car in every garage and a _____ in every pot." *chicken*
20) A nick-name for New York City is the big: *apple*
21) Providing food for the family's needs is providing the: *bread and butter*
22) Santa's belly shook like a bowl full of: *jelly*
23) Someone very likable might be said to be as sweet as: *pie or honey*
24) If you accidentally sit on your hat, you squash it flat as a: *pancake*
25) A pretty girl might be called some: *cookie*

26) A person who's not very smart might be called an: _____ head. *egg*
27) George Washington's father was furious when he cut down a ----- tree. *cherry*

Bible questions

1) What city was the birthplace of Paul? *Tarsus*
2) What young man played the harp to soothe King Saul? *David*
3) What creature was the first to leave the ark? *dove.*
4) Who sat at the feet of the teacher Gamaliel? *Paul*
5) Who commanded Dorcas to come alive from the dead? *Peter*
6) Who was almost persuaded to become a Christian? *Felix*
7) Who were the people who passed through the Red Sea? *Israelites*
8) Name the four gospels. *Matthew, Mark, Luke* and *John*
9) What book in the Bible contains wise sayings? *Proverbs*
10) Where was Jesus born? *Bethlehem*
11) What was the town He lived in? *Nazareth*
12) What is the first book of the Bible? *Genesis*
13) What is the last book? *Revelations*
14) What are songs and poems written by David? *Psalms*
15) What famous prayer did Jesus teach us? *The Our Father*
16) How many apostles were there? *12 + 1 later*
17) Who was the one who hung himself? *Judas*
18) Who replaced him? *Matthias*
19) How did Jesus die? *by crucifixion*
20) Which apostle denied Jesus? *Peter*
21) Which one was known as the doubter? *Thomas*
22) What holiday today celebrates Jesus' rising from the dead? *Easter*

Wedding fun and superstitions

- married in white, you've chosen right
- married in red, you'd be better dead
- married in yellow, ashamed of the fellow
- married in blue, your love is true
- married in green, ashamed to be seen
- married in black, you'll ride in a hack
- married in pearl, you'll live in a whirl
- married in pink, your spirits will sink
- married in brown, you'll live out of town

1) Why did brides long, long ago begin wearing veils at weddings? *To hide their faces so evil spirits wouldn't recognize them.*
2) Why was June chosen as the wedding month? *In Roman mythology, Juno, the goddess of women, was supposed to have blessed weddings in her month.*
3) Why, long ago, was rice first thrown at weddings? *To appease evil spirits and hopefully provide many children.*

Summary

These are just a few old familiar word games that residents have a lot of fun with. If you haven't already, why not begin to collect your own and put them into a binder to use for an afternoon's entertainment or for emergencies?. They can truly be a lifesaver for the professional activity director.

CHAPTER 12

Surviving December

December, for an activity director, is the most hectic month of the year. Any A.D. who gets through it and comes out smiling can rest assured that she can handle anything the rest of the year. Though busier than any other month, in one way, December calendar planning is easier than usual. You don't have to go after entertainment. It comes to you. Everyone thinks of nursing homes during the holiday season, so cash in on it. Build your files with names of people who might do programs for the rest of the year. Begin planning for the season as early as October. Seek press coverage for your facility during this season. It is easier to get than the rest of the year. A community project can draw the press. Decide on one with residents. Here's some examples: a party for underprivileged kids, putting on a Christmas play, offering a gift-wrapping service, providing a Christmas movie for kids, or having a drawing for something residents have made such as a quilt.

Continue to plan ahead

Stock up early on supplies you'll need during for the busy holiday season: film, candy, wrapping paper and decorations. Schedule early, important meetings on your December calendar. With the phone ringing fast and furious, it's easy to accidentally fill in those dates with other activity.

Decorating the facility

You'll probably want to begin decorating around the first of December. Schedule simple activities for a few days that won't require your constant attention so you can concentrate on decorating the facility. Make a statement with your decorations. If you are draping tinsel from the ceiling or around the fireplace or anywhere else, measure the distance between each loop. Write these measurements down on a three-by-five card and hold it until you pack away your Christmas decorations. Next year's decorating will be easier because you won't have to remeasure. It sounds tedious, but it will pay off. Take care with little things like hanging wall decorations at the same height down a hall. Don't over decorate. Residents will probably want to help decorate the trees. Even confused residents enjoy this. Supervision will be needed to have a nice finished look. You might try red bows, pine cones, and strung popcorn rather than the usual ornaments.

It's fun to have a theme in decorating. I once used an *old-fashioned Christmas* theme. Antique rocking chairs, a braided rug and old-time toys were set around the tree and near the fireplace. Decorating was natural using greenery, pine cones, popcorn, paper chains, gumdrop wreaths and decorated cookies. You might consider a *Teddy bear* theme with numerous bears spread throughout the facility dressed in various costumes. Invite children and adults one day to come for a *Teddy bear tea* and to bring their favorite Teddy. Give prizes for oldest, newest, largest, smallest, most unique, most worn and most loved.

Calendar planning

With decorating out of the way, you can next devote your attention to calendar planning. You seldom have to worry about filling the first two weeks of December. There's an abundance of clubs, churches and various singing groups wanting to come and entertain residents. Teachers enjoy bringing students to visit during December. Take advantage of it. If they don't call, contact them.

Now look to the third week of December. By this time most people are busy with their own Christmas preparations. Consequently, you may have to do more hands-on entertainment this week. This is a good time to schedule special Christmas movies that can often be borrowed from your local library. A day might be set aside for residents to bake and decorate cookies. If your budget allows, you might buy cookie dough in rolls and use prepared frosting. Or you might buy sugar cookies and let residents decorate them. Fudge or other candy can be made, with residents watching or helping, using an electric cooking pot.

Close to Christmas, you'll probably want to have a big Christmas party for residents with Santa coming and passing out wrapped gifts. These can be donated bingo prizes or gifts donated by churches and sororities earlier in December and set aside for this purpose. Also, a Christmas tea (not the same as the Teddy bear tea) is good for one afternoon's activity. It doesn't have to be fancy-- just cookies and punch and maybe a reminiscence session with residents talking about Christmases long past.

Keeping things neat

Many gifts, as we said before, are brought into the nursing home during December, and it's up to the activity director to find a place to put them. Difficult as it is when you are so busy, take a minute to keep things orderly. It will help much when you need to retrieve items quickly.

Welcome your guests

You'll probably have guests visit your facility daily to entertain residents. Since many of these are first-time visitors, you will benefit yourself and your residents by lavishing a little extra attention on them. As we said before, *you* represent your facility; and the impression you give them, good or bad, will be carried out into the community. Try to get their names, addresses and phone numbers. If a group, ask for a contact person. Put this information on three-by-five cards in your files for potential future programs.

It's Christmas

Finally it's Christmas! It's time for you to enjoy your *own* holiday. Don't feel guilty that you are not at the facility to entertain your residents on the *big* day. They've had a whole month of Christmas activity, and now it's your turn for a special day. Anyway, the kitchen sees to it that the residents have a special dinner and many of them will have family visitors.

December's not over yet

You may breathe a sigh of relief with the big holiday over but you're not through the month yet. There's few volunteers the week following Christmas, and you are probably too worn out to plan really big events. Try holding simple activities the last week of the month: sing-a-longs, another holiday movie, a simple craft. On the last day of the year, it's fun to have a *Good-bye 19--* party rather than a *New Year's* party. Many activity directors have New Year's Day off, anyway.

It's wise to send out thank you notes to those who have entertained or done nice things for your residents. A short, personal note of appreciation often works better than packaged thank you notes because can people see your sincerity and gratefulness. This encourages them to return again. It's nearly impossible, though, to keep up with written thank you's to all the carolling groups.

Storing decorations

When the month is over and it's time to take down decorations, grab your camera. If you haven't already done it, go about your facility and take pictures of every decorated area. Use a Polaroid, or have them developed quickly. Now take decorations down carefully storing each area's decorations in a separate plastic bag. In this bag, include the photo of that area and the three-by-five card with the proper measurements you recorded when you hung the decorations. One bag or decorations might be labeled *stairway*, another one, *fireplace*; and still another *downstairs front hall*. Using this method, *anyone* can put up the decorations exactly as you want them.

Summary

The Christmas season is certainly a challenge to an activity director, but it's no reason to become harried and overworked. With proper planning, the season can be a real joy not only for your residents and visitors, but for you as well. After all, you gave them one terrific month of holiday activities, so sit back and pat yourself on the back for a job well done.

CHAPTER *13*

Creative Christmas Community Outreaches That the Press Can't Resist

At Christmas time hearts have a way of turning to those in long-term care facilities. Consequently, the press are always looking for human-interest stories which will touch the hearts of their readers. Here's your chance. You can create that story for them. One excellent goal for a professional activity director is to obtain, every Christmas season, a good story in the newspaper (preferably front page) and television coverage, as well. Since the press are seeking such a story, why not take advantage of this opportunity to promote your facility? Here's a few ideas that have been successful and have brought excellent press coverage in newspapers, magazines and on television. You will, no doubt, recognize these stories. In Chapter five you read the actual press releases that promoted them. In this chapter, the events themselves, and the how-to's of them, are discussed in case you wish to try them in your facility.

Dressing the babies

Have your residents make simple baby gowns from tiny Christmas print flannelette. Present these gowns to your local hospital to be given to all the new babies born during the holiday season. Don't worry if you have only a few residents able to sew; you can still do this. (Three committed ladies turned out seventy-five hand-sewn baby gowns in three month's time at my facility.)

A yard of material will make about three gowns. They don't have to be very big for newborns. Of course, babies come in all sizes so make at least three sizes. Perhaps you or a volunteer could sew up on a machine the shoulder and side seams and leave just the hemming of the neck, arms and bottom for residents. When the sewing is finished, add two strips of one-fourth inch wide ribbon to the neck for a tie. Lace can be added if you wish.

Before you undertake this project, first contact your hospital's public relations department. They will probably welcome the free publicity for them and your facility will love it, too. It's always a thrill for residents when the new mothers send thank-you notes and include pictures of their babies wearing the gowns they made. These photographs can be displayed on a bulletin board for all to see.

Reaching out to the world

These baby gowns can be made in the same way and sent off to babies in the third world through an agency such as *Catholic Relief Services.* Residents are especially blessed to know that they are helping to clothe babies who may never again in their lives receive another *new* piece of clothing.

Baby dolls for impoverished children

One never outgrows the need to give. Residents in a long-term care facility *receive* much at Christmas time, but they enjoy even more *giving* of themselves to others. Too often, though, that need cannot be satisfied and they find themselves only on the receiving end. You, as activity director, can change that for them. One way is by letting them help make baby dolls for impoverished children.

The dolls are made from boys crew socks--either plain white or the ones with colored bands stripes at the top. Buy the ones that have a heel in them, not tube socks. This heel becomes the doll's bottom. Sock number one becomes the body and legs of the doll. Sock number two becomes the arms. First go to sock number two. Separate with scissors were the ribbing joins the foot of the sock. (The foot piece of this sock may be saved for another project like crocheting around the edge to make footies.) Use only the ribbed part (plain or with colored stripes). Split this in two lengthwise to create two pieces which become arms. Have residents sew the arm side seam and one end. The other end is left open for stuffing with batting. Let residents stuff it and later attach to the doll.

Now, take the first sock. Center the heel of the sock in the middle of the back to create a bottom for the doll. Holding it this way, with scissors, from the bottom (actual top of the sock) cut lengthwise up as far as where the ribbing joins the foot section. This forms the two legs which are still attached to the body. Even confused residents can stuff these dolls. When the body is stuffed, sew up the edges of both legs leaving a little open space at the crotch for turning. When turned, stuff and top stick the crotch. Residents who are good at sewing can gather a little around the upper part of the sock after it has been stuffed to create a neck and head. Then use a permanent marker or embroider closed baby doll eyes (these look like two c"s on their back side). Use a red marker or embroider a tiny red dot for the baby's mouth. Fashion a miniature flannel baby gown and bonnet for each doll. These dolls can be given to a local community center or any group that will get them to underprivileged children. (A word of caution: staff and visitors will fall in love with the dolls and want to buy them.)

This is a good human-interest story because those who are confined themselves are shown reaching out to help others whom they feel are less fortunate. If possible, let residents have a part in personally delivering their gifts.

Take a chance

Have someone build a life-size Barbie doll house and have residents decorate it and make furniture for it. It's important to have this finished very early in December so that it can be on display for all who come to your facility during the holiday season. As you advertise the drawing for this house, stress that any child under ten (or whatever age you choose), can come in and sign up to win if she is accompanied by an adult. This will serve two purposes. First, it will keep unaccompanied children from overrunning your facility. Second, it will bring in, for a first-hand look, adults who may never otherwise visit your facility.

You will need someone with a little carpentry ability for the actual building of the house. It should be about three-and-a-half feet tall, three or four feet long and about eighteen-inches deep. It can be divided into two or three stories and into several rooms. Once the frame is built, bring it into your facility, and keep it visible so everyone can watch its progress. Have residents paint the inside if they are able. Get wallpaper samples and attach it to some walls. Collect free carpet and linoleum samples to glue them on the floors. Have residents make little curtains and hang them on dowel rods which are then attached at the windows. Other residents may be able to crochet tiny throw rugs.

Then comes the fun part. Let your imagination run free in the building of furniture and the making of accessories such as lamps and pictures for the walls. Save plastic squirt tops and caps from detergent bottles for planters, wastebaskets and lamp shades. Use tiny box lids for miniature picture frames and glue little pictures cut from magazines inside them. Get cut pieces of wood such as two-by-fours from the scrap box at a lumber yard. Nail these together for couches and chairs. Cover them with foam and scrap fabric. Use a staple gun to secure the material. Tables can be made with small pieces of wood using clothes pins or dowel rods for legs.

Finish the outside of the house however you like. You might want to paint it gray, and glue white painted popsicle sticks around the outside to represent a picket fence. Use small boxes and glue them under the windows for flower boxes. Give your house a name that has something to do with your facility's name. That way, when it goes out into the community, your facility will still be remembered by all who see it. When your house is completed, buy Barbie dolls to occupy it. It's nice to have a family--father, mother, child, and at least one baby. You'll probably want to make one room of your house a nursery. You might want to a buy plastic cradle for this room.

Send a tempting press release to all the media when you are about half-finished. Tell them of your project because they'll probably want to cover the story in the house's formative stages. Getting this doll house finished will require a lot of work from you, the activity director, but it's fun work and will bring many people into your facility to see it. Residents can hardly wait to get to the activity room each morning, either to work on it or just to check on its progress.

Have a party

Christmas is a wonderful time to involve the underprivileged children of your community. Try holding a big party for them and provide a Christmas at your facility that they may not otherwise have. Where do you get the money for this, you might ask? It's not that difficult. In September or October, call local men's service organizations such as Kiwanas, Rotary, Optimists, Moose, Eagles, American Legion and Knights of Columbus. Also call philanthropic sororities and fraternities if you like. Tell them your residents want to give a party for poor children but lack the funds. Ask if they'd like to be a part. Be sure to tell them that their assistance will be acknowledged in any publicity you acquire concerning the event. Ask for a specific figure. A hundred dollars from each one is not unreasonable. If they say they can't afford your asking figure, ask if they would be willing to make any donation. Check with some local stores for donations of candy, games, fruit, soda pop and other gifts. Sorority and fraternity members might be willing to do your party shopping for you.

Involve your residents in the planning, wrapping of the children's gifts, and the filling of stockings. Arrange for a piano player for the party so the kids and the old folks can sing Christmas carols together. You might have Santa Claus arrive and sit in a special chair just for him. He can then gather the children around him and read them a story--perhaps of the Christ child's coming at that first Christmas.

Check thoroughly so that you get *really* underprivileged children. At Christmas there are many organizations helping and some children receive from several organizations while others can be missed completely. When you know who, what ages, and how many children will be coming, you can decide what you will buy them. Socks, warm mittens and hats are always welcome. A couple toys are nice to give, along with smaller gifts like coloring books and crayons.

Just quilting

Here's another project that requires sewing but it goes quickly and will bring the public into your facility. Have your residents cut out six-inch blocks of fabric in many colors and patterns and sew them together to make comforter-quilts. It's nice to make two twin-bed quilts--one in pastel colors for girls and one in bright bold colors for boys. Buy a new twin-size sheet that will be used for the backing, and measure the assembled blocks to fit its size. A layer of quilt batting is put between the sewn-together blocks and the new sheet. Then all three thicknesses are pinned together with large quilting pins. Rather than quilting, residents can knot and tie these with yarn which actually makes them comforters rather quilts.

When they are finished, use public service announcements to advertise your event. Also send out press releases announcing that your facility is holding a drawing for kids and will be giving the comforters away before Christmas. This may well be a better visual story considering the colorful quilts. Many times T.V. stations are in need of just one short story to finish off the evening news. Help them.

Summary

When seeking a Christmas project that will involve your residents and bring you good media coverage, planning is the key. Begin thinking as early as September or October what you'll do for your Christmas community outreach project. Involve your residents as much as you can, but know the brunt of every big project will fall on your shoulders. Don't be afraid of a little extra work. That is what will make you and your program stand out among the others in your area. If you continue in your position for several years, your community will be watching expectantly each Christmas season to see just what new project your facility will be tackling that year. Don't let them down. Through these Christmas outreaches, you not only get the community's eyes on your facility, but you once again affirm to your residents that they are worthwhile individuals and are still a productive and vital part of their community.

CHAPTER *14*

Making Your Newsletter Better

All too often the job of producing a newsletter falls upon the activity director. And that is fine if she enjoys writing and research and has a feeling for lay-out and design. But what about those other activity directors who detest writing and put out a newsletter merely to satisfy the demands of their administrator? For these, I'd offer a word of encouragement: "You don't have to be a writer to put out a first-class newsletter."

Why even have a newsletter?

Let's first look at the advantages of having a newsletter. As activity director, you have it in your power, through your newsletter, to greatly enhance your facility's image in the community and beyond. It is perhaps your greatest public relations tool--if you know how to utilize it to the fullest. When the community talks positively about your facility's newsletter and look forward to each issue, and when new patients arrive at your facility because they have enjoyed your newsletter, it reflects positively on you. It also helps to establish your professionalism. Editing your facility's newsletter gives you a chance to meet new people and to interview them. This, in turn, involves you more in the community and the community becomes more involved with your facility.

Evaluating and improving

Perhaps you've never done a newsletter and want to know how to begin. Or maybe you've been doing one for some time but would like to improve it. Let's take a look at some ways to do both. First, if you have already edited a newsletter, get a copy of one you've done, and let's go over it together. If you haven't done one to this point, find someone else's newsletter to evaluate.

A good newsletter contains three basic qualities: accuracy, interest, and good taste. Does yours meet these qualifications? Is it readable? Are their typos? Incorrect punctuation? If so, try having someone else proofread your newsletter before it goes to print. It's difficult to proofread your own work. Is the material interesting? Is it fresh and suitable for your readership? To answer this question, you must determine *who* you want to read it--residents? families? doctors? business men? libraries? schools? your community? other states? When your readership is determined, you can better plan its contents.

Naming your newsletter

Does your newsletter have a catchy name? What do you want to express in its name? Newspaper and newsletter names are often built around a word which expresses communication. Here's an example: journal, review, bulletin, post, focus, outlook, guide, spotlight, wire, trends, scope, forecast, update, courier, alert, times, happenings, event or report. You might join one these with your facility's name. Or you could select a name related to your facility's purpose for being--*Health Care Update, Senior's Spotlight* or *Retirement Review.* If all else fails, libraries carry a book called the *National Directory of Newsletters and Reporting Services* put out by Gale Research Company. Another one is the *Newsletter*

Yearbook Directory put out by National Research Bureau. Browsing through these, you'll see thousands of names that others have chosen. Perhaps you can gather ideas for your own newsletter's name.

The front page

Take a good look at your front page? What about your nameplate where your newsletter's name and logo (if you have one) are located. Does your nameplate take up at least one-fourth of the page? It is more impressive if it does. Is your company's name, address and phone number somewhere on the nameplate or very close to it? This is important should one want to contact your facility perhaps to place a resident there. Your name should be on it as editor, and the frequency of its publication should be noted. If you copyright your newsletter, that notice could be on the nameplate. You may want to put your nameplate in a box to make it stand out. The nameplate is the first impression one gets of your newsletter so it's important the lettering be neat and easy to read. If you do the newsletter in-house without a computer and font program, you can still have nice large letters. Rub-off letters purchased at an office supply store will do the trick. Your nameplate will remain the same on each newsletter so create a *master* nameplate. Paste it up each issue before copying the newsletter or sending it to the printer.

Are your margins about an inch wide on each side? You don't want them too narrow or too wide. For vertical margins, allow at least an inch at the top and at the bottom. Is there an article on your front page to *hook* your reader? In other words, is there something there that would make one, regardless of his age, sex or occupation, want to read further? An article here which crosses all readership lines is excellent. Save less important material for a later page. Your administrator's name and all department heads can be listed on the front page if you wish. If not there, they should at least be printed somewhere in your newsletter.

Headlines

Does your front page and the rest of your newsletter contain clear, concise headlines? Well-written headlines can quickly draw a reader into the body of your newsletter which is what you are trying to achieve. When writing headlines, try to put them in the present tense even though the events spoken about may have already happened such as: *ABC Facility Competes in Olympics.* Make headlines brief. Put the subject before the verb. *Patient Wins.* Seek to get a clear message across and avoid cliches and cute talk.

Illustrations

Pictures or illustrations on the front page can be beneficial--if they are good ones. Quality art work uplifts your publication by making it appear more professional. If they are not good photos, you give your reader negative feelings about your publication, and your facility. Don't use photos randomly. They must serve a vital purpose--to illustrate an article, to give information, to honor someone, or to express a needed emotion. Learn to use a good 35mm camera or find someone who can. It is valuable to you as an activity director to invest in a photography class. You can obtain free or inexpensive photos on many subjects from various places such as libraries, businesses, and the U.S. Government (check library for addresses). Clear black and white photos copy best. Try for action shots. Consider the background when taking pictures. Occasionally, a facility newsletter will use a simple "coloring book-type" drawing. This might cause an adult to take that newsletter less seriously.

Clip-art can be used effectively in newsletters to break the solid print appearance, to express seasons, and to enhance the over-all appearance of the newsletter. You must be careful, though, not to over-do it, or you'll lose the professional image you are seeking.

Type

Take a look at the overall appearance of the newsletter. How about the type? Is it too small or too large? Extra-large print may be good if the newsletter is to go *only* to residents, but the oversize print may cause your newsletter to be taken less seriously by the community at large. Studies show that using all capital letters make reading difficult. You may send your newsletter out and have it typeset and printed, or you may type it yourself and copy it on the copy machine. Either way is effective, as long as it is neat.

Examine the contents

Now, let's take a look at contents. What is in your newsletter that would cause one to want to read it. Again, you must determine your readership before you can determine content. If you are merely putting out an in-house newsletter, it's okay to use things like birthdays, get-well wishes and lost- and-found articles. If you want to reach out beyond your facility and your community, present subjects of interest to a wider readership. Let your readers know you are always seeking news. Exchange newsletters with other activity directors throughout the country, and gather ideas from one another. For lay-out ideas, collect other newsletters not pertaining exclusively to activity directing. Keep an *idea* file in your drawer, and throughout the month, add things you might want to use sometime. It's always valuable to include your residents in articles. A resident interview of the month may be good if you do an in-depth one. Ask about life in their childhood--what their schools were like, what their chores were as children, what they remember about their grandparents, and what they remember about World War I and II.

Do research at the library. Newsletter content ideas might include: words of wisdom, famous quotes, old proverbs, old-time remedies for ailments, quotes by Will Rogers, or Burma Shave messages used along the highways in the fifties. If you don't like this reminiscent angle, you might try slanting it more medical. Research subjects of interest along this line. You may want to fill your newsletter with various puzzles to be solved.

If you are not one who enjoys writing, have others write your newsletter for you. You might have the director of nurses do a monthly article on something about medicine. You might have your maintenance man do an article offering hints to make home maintenance easier. Your dietary supervisor could do a column on cooking and include a recipe. Perhaps your chaplain would write something of a spiritual nature each month. Some administrators enjoy doing a column or can at least be talked into it. They may know just what to write about, or you may have to give them a subject. Perhaps: *What's involved in being a nursing home administrator?* This could include duties, education, headaches and satisfactions. He might write on the good results obtained from the most recent state survey or the spirit of cooperation in the facility.

Most activity directors include a calendar of events in their newsletter. This can be good, but at the same time, if you have more interesting reading for the space taken up by a calendar, try a *What's Happening* column. In it, highlight your *special* events, forgetting the run-of-the-mill activities. That way you don't waste your reader's time with non-essentials.

If you want to broaden your readership, begin to interview community people and experts in various fields. The local police chief might talk about programs they offer the community such as school visits or how to mark valuables. The fire chief could be interviewed about providing tours for seniors and children, their Christmas toy-repair project, or what they do when they have nothing to do. The mayor might be interviewed about the problem of elderly living alone without proper supervision and possibly endangering themselves. A teacher might discuss the value of the younger and older generations doing things together. A supplier of wheel chairs might explain some of the special needs of the elderly and tell of the equipment available and how to best care for it. The governor could even be interviewed, either in person or by letter on any subject pertaining to the elderly.

Interviewing tips

By gathering interviews you are saving yourself from having to locate all your material personally. Before you interview a subject, plan carefully. Prepare open-ended questions that can't be answered with a yes or no. Remember your reader when asking the questions. Do a little research on the person you are interviewing *before* the interview. This allows you to ask better questions and adds depth to your story. Make an appointment, and be early. Ask permission to tape so you get the quotes right. A personal interview is great, but phone interviews will do the trick and are more practical for the busy activity director. In personal interviews, though, you can notice gestures and expressions that help you paint a word picture of your subject. Gather more information than needed. Start out with a question that will make your subject comfortable and not feel threatened. Ask for a photo. As soon as you get back to your office, write the piece while the information is fresh in your mind. Mention the surroundings, how the subject felt, how you felt, and the information talked about. There's no need to let your subject read the article before publication.

Building your mailing list

It's important to continue to build your mailing list and to keep it current. Always include families of new residents. Some doctors like interesting newsletters in their waiting rooms and especially if they see patients at your facility. If your newsletter is such that business men would find it interesting, by all means, put them on your list. Many families of residents, or former residents who have moved out of state, still enjoy receiving an interesting newsletter. If you always have something informative, enlightening, or entertaining inside, word will spread quickly and others will likely *ask* to be on your mailing list. Your list might also include other health care facilities, lawyers, hospitals, social service agencies, policemen, firemen, politicians, schools, churches of all denominations and even the governor.

Summary

It's not easy to edit a quality newsletter but it's not that difficult either. It's simply a matter of trial and error--of knowing your readership and seeking to meet their needs. So even if you aren't a writer, why not give it another try? It certainly is a good feeling when your administrator announces that his newest resident came to your facility because someone picked up a copy of your newsletter in a doctor's office just when they were in the market for a good long-term care facility. When you develop a quality newsletter that improves the census, you might be in a position to bargain for another pay raise.

CHAPTER *15*

Volunteers: The Activity Director's Right Hand

You have a mammoth job to do. You're a department of one--or possibly two or three or more. There's no way you can accomplish all your duties without help. Unfortunately, few facilities can provide enough paid employees to meet the many demands of their activity department. Where does an activity director turn? There's only one answer--an excellent volunteer program.

Volunteer coordinating very often falls under the activity director's jurisdiction. Perhaps you are fortunate to have stepped into a position with a good volunteer program already in operation. Still, maybe you would like to improve on it a bit. Or possibly you don't have a volunteer program established at all but would like to start one. Just where do you begin?

Evaluating your needs

Allow yourself desk time to do some serious research and planning. Ask yourself these questions:

- How much time do I have to train and oversee a program?
- Can I identify a variety of worthwhile jobs for them to do?

- What do I want in a volunteer?
- Will I personally handle the program, or will I have an assistant or a volunteer to do it for me?
- Where can I find volunteers?
- How can I keep them?
- How will staff respond to volunteers?
- What qualifications will I seek in volunteers?
- How will I keep track of their time?
- Do I have a volunteer form ready for applicants to fill out?
- Can I fire a volunteer who doesn't work out?

Running a volunteer program does take time, but it is time well spent. It's an investment in your activity program and in your facility as a whole. Any activity director owes it to herself to at least give a good volunteer program a try.

Why would someone want to *give* their time away?

The reasons are many and varied. A senior citizen might volunteer to be with other people and to constructively fill free hours. Volunteering allows that individual to remain useful in the community and to give. It can also bring recognition, a basic need in many people.

A middle-aged man or woman might volunteer to broaden his or her horizons, to gain new skills, or to make broader contacts. Volunteering can also bring the self-confidence that may be lacking in their lives.

Working people volunteer, too. Singles may have lonely hours to fill after work. Volunteering can soothe that loneliness. It gives them an opportunity to reach out beyond their hurt and loneliness and give of their time and talents. Volunteering helps them acquire new skills that may be useful later on. If their regular job is unsatisfying, volunteering may compensate.

Homemakers volunteer for many reasons. Being cooped up day after day, with only small children to talk to is challenging, indeed-- and sometimes lonely. Volunteering offers these homemakers an opportunity to get out and to broaden their horizons. They meet new people. They learn new skills that may later be useful in the job market. Volunteering can also build self-esteem. Since homemakers pursue many interests working women can't, they have much to offer residents. Older homemakers, after children have left home, may feel unneeded. Volunteering helps meet the need to give, and to help others.

High school students volunteer for many reasons. They have much energy and some free hours to spend. Many have working parents, and rather than going home to an empty house, would prefer doing something useful. Some just love the elderly and want to share their love. Some have special talents like art or music they'd like to share with the lonely and confined. Some may be considering a career in health care and are career shopping. Others may volunteer as a special project for school.

College students might volunteer for some of the same reasons as high school students. They are probably more seriously pursuing career goals, and they may want to experience working in a long-term-care facility first-hand. They may volunteer as part of a course credit.

Young adults volunteer to meet people, to learn new skills or because they are interested in special problems. They may simply love the elderly and want to share their time and talents with them. They may volunteer to combat loneliness and boredom.

What will I have them do?

Every facility has specific needs for volunteers but many are common to all. Let's classify some types of volunteers:

- one-on-one volunteers
- specific-area volunteers
- all-purpose volunteers
- office worker volunteer
- group leader volunteer
- creative volunteer

These are just a few sample classifications. You can probably come up with many more. When a volunteer begins, her first question is usually: "What will I do?" That question is best answered by her. What does she like to do? Is she a person who likes to do crafts? cook? type? work with groups? be a leader? be a behind-the-scenes person? Is she creative? Is she an organizer? Does she like to raise money, or not mind asking for donations? Does she like to make phone calls? Does she like administrative-type duties? Does she enjoy working closely with residents? Let's look at some of these categories of volunteers:

ONE-ON-ONE VOLUNTEER

One-on-one volunteers might enjoy reading to residents, painting their fingernails or curling their hair. They might play cards--even something simple like *Old Maid.* They could be provided with materials to work with confused residents--perhaps a jar of buttons which the resident could separate according to color, size and shape. Using magazines, they can help a resident identify various pictures. They can also make a scrapbook with a resident on a specific subject such as *babies,* by using pictures torn from magazines. One-on-one volunteers can go room-to-room and just visit residents. They can help residents polish their shoes or take them out for a walk. They can color or paint a picture with them. The list is limitless. You can always find jobs for this type of volunteer.

SPECIFIC-AREA VOLUNTEER

Most people have one area of interest which they enjoy more than others. Try to get volunteers to share that interest with residents on a regular basis. An example of this might be someone who loves crafts. Some volunteers are more comfortable giving demonstrations rather than involving residents in the actual process. A specific-area volunteer might play the piano or guitar, do cake-decorating or show their vacation movies. They might lead a kitchen band, do poetry reading, dance for residents or do their mending. This type of volunteer will come regularly--once a month or more often.

ALL-PURPOSE VOLUNTEER

If you find one of these, you find a jewel. An all-purpose volunteer will do whatever is needed--wherever it is needed. They will transport residents to and from activities, run errands, help out at evening parties, accompany you on outings and help serve a picnic lunch at your facility. All-purpose volunteers like flexibility. All you have to do is ask when you need them. Some will be willing to come every day; others will come only when needed.

OFFICE WORKER VOLUNTEER

Some volunteers have time to give but do not enjoy working closely with residents. Put them to work doing things for you. They might type your newsletter, run copies, make trips to the post office or make party invitations. They may keep your activity cupboards in order, update your mailing list, do correspondence or address envelopes. Senior citizens who have previously worked in offices enjoy this type of work. Sometimes you'll find a resident who will make a wonderful office volunteer.

GROUP LEADER VOLUNTEER

Some people are born leaders; others can be trained to be group leaders. These volunteers are valuable because they free you from leading all activities personally. A senior volunteer might lead a reminiscence group. A younger person could also do it with the

135

right materials. This volunteer might hold a spelling bee, do other word games, or put on a video for residents. They may make popcorn or home-made ice cream. They might call bingo, lead an exercise group, or do a cooking project.

CREATIVE VOLUNTEER

A creative volunteer, for you, is like another pair of hands. They usually have some artistic ability or at least a good discerning eye. They can hang decorations and do bulletin boards in a way that doesn't look thrown together. They can make name tags and birthday notices and decorate residents' doors. They can keep your facility looking attractive and cheerful. A former teacher is good as this kind of volunteer.

Who will handle the volunteer program?

As we said before, coordinating the volunteer program usually falls in activity director's lap. If so, do you personally desire to carry out the actual duties of it? Many activity directors enjoy this aspect of their job very much; others do not. If that's the case, perhaps you can find a volunteer who will supervise the other volunteers for you. A volunteer supervisor must get along well with others and have the ability to designate. This person is answerable directly to you.

Recruiting volunteers

With more and more of the adult population working, where does one find volunteers? True, it *is* more difficult today to find volunteers than fifteen years ago, but they *are* available--if you know where to look. First, check the volunteer bureau, if your city has one. They match volunteers with agencies.

Then actively recruit them. Visit senior centers and describe your activity program and your particular needs. Schools, too, are an excellent source of volunteers. Junior high and high school students have much to offer residents and your facility in general. Go to the schools and share about your program. If you can present a slide show or video of your residents in various activities, it will be a great help in recruiting volunteers. You might visit a particular class or department. The school newspaper staff, yearbook staff or the English department might provide some volunteers to help on your newsletter. The coaches and individual sports departments may provide volunteers to demonstrate weight-lifting, wrestling or gymnastics in your facility. The art department might supply decorations for your facility, or some of the students might come to your facility and work on art projects with residents.

As we all know, churches are great places to find volunteers. Call many of them, or send out letters expressing your needs. You can also ask the churches to run a note in their bulletins asking for volunteers.

Courts sometimes sentence small offenders to do community service as their penalty. Volunteering in a long-term-care facility is one way they can pay their debt to society. If your facility has no objections to the program, you might want to try it. There can be a few problems, though. The biggest one I've experienced is the offenders not always showing up when expected. As these offenders come from all walks of life, you can expect to uncover many talents within them.

Local clubs, sororities and fraternities provide great volunteers. If you have a college nearby, utilize their bulletin boards to present your volunteer needs. Call the different schools or departments to seek volunteers. Frequently home extension clubs do things for, or with, residents. Also call your local *YMCA* and *YWCA* who sometime have groups and individuals willing to provide an activity. And, finally, there are always public service announcements on radio and free columns in the newspaper where you can ask for volunteers.

Assessing the potential volunteer

When potential volunteers come into your office, you must determine if they will be an asset or a liability to your facility. Sometimes volunteers are not employable elsewhere and have a host of personal and emotional problems when they come to you. If you are willing to give them a chance and are patient with them, some make excellent volunteers. Many of them don't. You just have to use your best judgment.

Develop a form for potential volunteers to fill out during the interview. Get the necessary personal information and their areas of interest. Also, secure the name of a contact person in case of emergency, and see that they provide references. Assess the applicant carefully? Are they neat? What is their motive for volunteering? Is there a place for them in your facility? Do they have a particular area of interest that would make them valuable to your program? Do you foresee any potential problems? You might want to jot down impressions you get while interviewing them. When they leave you can look over their form and assess whether they will meet your needs.

Beware of an over-eager volunteer--one who immediately wants to come in every day or every week. Though there are exceptions, in many cases, this volunteer lasts only a short time as they quickly burn out or find they don't want that great a commitment. It's best to tell them to give it a try a little less frequently at first. Let them know you'll review their work and discuss more hours at a later time.

If during the interview, you feel very confident about them as a volunteer, you may want to accept them on the spot. But there is an advantage to telling them that you will review their application and get back to them. This gives you time to check their references and to think about them as a potential volunteer and where you'd place them.

Training

The best way to lose a volunteer is by neglecting to tell them *exactly* what their duties are. Every volunteer needs a specific job description. Pre-printed forms are available, but you may need to individualize them for volunteers. Each new volunteer should be given a facility handbook so they will know what is, and what isn't allowed in the facility. If yours is a small facility, you might want to train each volunteer individually. This may require several days effort on your part. Some volunteer coordinators wait until there is a group of volunteers and train them together. They begin with a tour, then offer a film or slide show of their activity program in progress. They discuss the procedures in their facility and tell of the duties expected of them as volunteers. The more thoroughly a volunteer is initially screened and trained, the more likely he or she will be to remain and be a valuable asset to your department.

It's extremely important that volunteers be accountable to someone. Find out what hours to expect them and see that those hours are honored. If they cannot come, make them aware that you expect them to call you so you can make other arrangements for their duties. Provide a sign-in book for them to record their arrival and departure times, and what they did. Introduce new volunteers to the staff, and inform the staff of just what each volunteer will be doing. It's important that nurses and aides are not caught off guard wondering why a unknown person is involving themselves with residents.

Recognition

It's wonderful for staff to be recognized and rewarded, but it's absolutely vital for volunteers. This is their only form of reimbursement so spare no opportunity to pat them on the back. This can be done verbally when you see them doing a good job. It can be a personal thanks every time they say good-bye to you upon leaving. It can take the form of an occasional personal note of thanks or small gifts such as a fresh flower in a vase, a coupon for a free meal or a magazine subscription. A yearly recognition dinner and party for all your volunteers is very important. It can be as simple or as formal as your budget allows. The dinner gives volunteers an opportunity to meet each other and to be publicly recognized. It's a chance to brag a little about each one of them, to recognize the hours they have given, and to present them with a certificate and possibly a gift. This is often the highlight of the year for your volunteers. It's worth all the time, effort and expense you put into it.

Summary

A volunteer program can add to your work load, but it will greatly expand your activity program. A well-managed volunteer program allows you to switch from leading all activities yourself to acting as coordinator of those who do lead them. In turn, you are free to spend more time at your desk charting, improving your newsletter, planning bigger and better activities or promoting your facility's name in your community. A professional activity director soon learns that she cannot do it all. She must delegate. And that is where the volunteer program comes in. Develop it fully, and those about you will no doubt begin to recognize you as an activity *director* and not just a fun and games lady who calls bingo and holds birthday parties. It will also make your job a whole lot easier.

CHAPTER *16*

Beating Burnout

There are few long-time activity directors who will not at some time in their career find the ugly disease of burnout creeping up on them. But when it does, a professional activity director will have some solutions in her bag of tricks. She'll be ready to meet the monster head on rather than be trampled underfoot and defeated by it. Before she can defeat her enemy, though, she must first know all she can about it. Like many other diseases, burnout is sneaky. It doesn't happen all at once but comes very gradually. Then, before you're even aware of what's happening, it has you firmly in its control.

One of the prime factors in burnout for activity directors is poor staff relations. This is often triggered by a lack of communication. Another reason is that activity directors, who give so much of themselves, begin to feel taken for granted. It seems no one appreciates their efforts, and they receive criticism when they are giving their very best. Another cause is that after working for many years, their job has become routine and is no longer challenging. There are many other reasons for the onset of burnout. No matter the reason, it's important to be one jump ahead of it when it strikes. Let's examine how burnout attacks an activity director.

It'll never happen to me

You love your job. There's so much to do. Your residents love you and need you. Your program is recognized and respected by the community. You have a wonderful administrator, and things are going great. You put in more hours than necessary, and nothing is too much to ask of you in regard to your job. This is probably one of the most wonderful, most exciting times in your career. Enjoy it. Sooner or later, though, this phase is likely to end.

Frustration

Everything has been going so well, but now you don't understand what's happening. A strange frustration has settled over you.

We all know the frustrating aspects of our profession. Too often activity directors are underpaid, occasionally receiving little more than aide's, though they are department heads with duties and responsibilities far broader. You work not only days but some evenings and weekends, as well. You may even have used your own money for projects when your activity budget was low or nonexistent. You find that other staff members don't always make your job easy. Though there are always invaluable and supportive staff members, you usually find in every facility some less cooperative ones. They offer unwarranted complaints and advice on how you *should* run your program. Being a department of one or two or three is difficult. Not only are you short-handed, but you often find yourself alone without another staff member who really understands your role--one in whom you can confide about the turmoil building within you. It's no wonder you become frustrated and burnout sets in.

Stagnation

This phase of burnout can be a dangerous area. Though you are working hard to meet your residents' needs and your administrator's wishes, your brewing frustration can lead you to a point of stagnation. You question within: *Why should I knock myself out if no one really cares? I can't seem to please anyone except my residents, anyway.* You decide to quit doing the little extra things you've always done--giving up a Sunday afternoon to visit lonely residents, or staying after hours because a sick resident wants *you* to be with her. You've always labored over planning special activities, but now you're content with mediocre ones. If you have little staff support and lots of complaints, you begin to entertain defeatist thoughts: *Maybe I'm not doing a good job. Maybe I'm not a value to this facility. Perhaps I am a failure after all.* And as you give in to this kind of thinking, you find yourself entering the next stage of burnout.

Indifference

You took this job to help residents, to make their life more fulfilling--and you're doing that. But residents are usually not the problem! It's just that no one else seems to understand or appreciate what you do. They are quick to criticize your efforts. So what was once an exciting career becomes simply a job--a job that is difficult to come to in the morning, and that welcomes departure in the afternoon. You find yourself pulling away, even from your residents whom you love dearly. You do the bare necessities--just enough to keep your job. You decide to forget about "going the extra mile" as you've done in the past. In the advanced stages of burnout, you may not even *be able* to do your job well.

So what's an activity director to do?

It's at this point that you must have a serious talk with yourself and begin to make some decisions. At this stage, there's a tendency to run, to change jobs, or to get out of the field of activities altogether. Changing to another facility is only a stop-gap measure. Soon the new job will develop a set of problems all its own, and you'll be right back where you started. Rather than looking outward for the solution to burnout, first look inward. Ask yourself some questions: *What has happened? Do I have any control over this situation? Do I want things to turn around? Do I want to recapture that early enthusiasm? What can I do about the problems I face? Where can I get someone to lift me up and be a support system for me? How can I gain back my self-worth? Can I begin to recognize myself for the professional I am? What can I do to gain the recognition and respect of others? How important is it to me that I have staff approval? Where do I begin?*

The road to recovery
BE GOOD TO YOURSELF

The first step toward healing is to make a friend of yourself. Though others may have put you or your program down, or conveyed that your job is an *easy* one, don't allow *yourself* to jump on you, too. Be good to yourself. Be your own best friend. Comfort yourself. Reward yourself. Talk to yourself: *I am a good activity director. I am a better-than-average activity director. I've learned many things.*

Have you let those who don't even understand activity directing decide about your abilities? It's time to overrule them. *You* are the authority in activities, and no matter what anyone else says about it, you are a good activity director. You know your department like no one else, and you know what's best for it. Once that's settled in your own mind, you need to reinforce it. When a negative thought comes, quickly replace it with a positive one: *I am okay. I am doing a good job. I have much to offer this facility. I will not be pushed from my job by anyone. When I leave, it will be because I want to leave, and for no other reason. I am doing a good job. I am an asset to this facility.*

Look good to feel good

As we said in chapter two, it's important to present the image of professionalism. This is especially true during burnout periods. An indifferent attitude toward the job often causes an activity director to dress more casually and less carefully than would be expected of a professional person. Put away the comfortable slacks, and buy yourself a new suit or dress. Splurge on a new hairdo. This alone will lift your spirits and help you feel better about yourself.

Get out of the rut

Do a total revamping of your activity program. Maybe you've gotten into a rut. Allow yourself plenty of time at your desk to work on this. Maybe you'll have to postpone a few regularly planned activities to make the time. That's okay! When a person is sick, she needs time to recuperate. You have had the disease of burnout. Allow yourself space and time to heal. You might want to change the times of your activities. Search out new ones that you have never tried. Do away, at least for a while, with some of the old standbys. Schedule some outings where you take a few residents who do not require a lot of care. Make it something fun and yet not too hard on yourself. This will get you out of the facility for a while and maybe help you to see things in a broader perspective. Spruce up your newsletter. See how you might improve your volunteer program. Redecorate your office or work area. Clean your desk and update your files. Take an inventory of all supplies on hand. This may spark some new ideas. Exchange ideas with other activity directors. Bring in new and fresh entertainment for your facility.

Build yourself a support system

If you have not already become involved in your district and state activity directors' associations, take advantage of this life line. Also check out the *National Association of Activity Professionals.*

These organizations are like a shot in the arm for activity directors. There you will find much support. No doubt, the other A.D.'s you meet there have already faced many of the problems you're facing. You'll find they have either conquered them, or at least learned to cope with them. Draw from their strength. Try never to skip a monthly meeting. That meeting should be the first thing scheduled on your calendar each month. If your administrator doesn't see the need for them, convince him. Tell him they are a safety valve to offset burnout. And burnout can cost him money in productivity and in training new help.

In the same manner, it is vital that you attend workshops and conventions prepared especially for activity directors. Even if the speakers are sharing about something you are not interested in, or something you already know, it's important to go anyway--to network. You meet other activity directors there, and you have a chance to share ideas and problems, failures and victories. Not only do the conventions and workshops give you a needed break from the day-to-day operations of your facility, but they fire you with fresh ideas and new enthusiasm. Never hesitate to pick up the phone and call another activity director when you need someone to unload on or to seek advice from. You'll find new strength and determination flowing into you before the conversation is over. There are few A.D.'s who are not willing to reach out and help another one, even if it's just to listen when you are having a bad day.

Schedule yourself time away

Though this may not appeal to everyone, it's helpful to divide up your vacation--for instance a week in January to recover from the hectic holiday season, and a week in July just to get away. These methods--taking outings with residents, attending activity director meetings and conventions, and splitting up your vacation--allow you regular time away from the facility. This helps you to recuperate from the constant demands of a rigorous and draining profession.

Summary

Burnout is like a virus. You can't see it, as we said before, but it creeps up on you when you least expect it. It's not like chicken pox that you get once and are immune to. It can return again and again if you don't protect yourself. But being forewarned is being forearmed. Just remember to be your own best friend, and don't expect everyone to like you or your program. Remember *you* are the authority on activities, and your opinion is the one that counts. Try to have good communication with your administrator. Maybe he will allow you to hold a monthly activity in-service for staff members to keep them in touch with your program and your goals. Seek his support because his is the opinion that matters the most. Learn to have a good *working* relationship with other staff members even if they don't give you the support you would like. And, finally, keep a varied program that doesn't allow you to get into a rut.

Burnout is an ugly disease, and there are times when your only option is to bow out, but for the most part, if you put your whole heart into fighting it, there's a better than average chance that you can beat it. And having beat it, you and your program will come out stronger than ever before.

CHAPTER *17*

The Professional Activity Director:
Who She *Really* Is

In the first chapter we discussed the "fun and games lady" and what she really does. Now let's take a look, not at what she *does*, but who she really *is*.

Big shoes to fill

As we said before, not everyone can be an activity director. Oh, they may be able to fill in for a few hours or a few days and entertain residents, but it takes a very unique person to fill the shoes of a professional activity director. There seems to be a special gift within her to equip her just for this task. She may not even know she possesses it until she has been an activity director for some time. Many attempt to be activity directors but soon find they do not have what it takes. They quickly fall by the wayside. Being a professional activity director is so much more than just a job. It's a career, a way of life, even a ministry. It provides an opportunity for inner exploring, inner growing, discovering what's really inside your heart and what's not. It allows you to uncover hidden strengths, values and weaknesses. It teaches you endurance, patience, compassion, inventiveness, thrift and unselfishness.

To present a first-hand look of what's really in the heart of a professional activity director, we interviewed several Indiana A.D.'s, many of them in the field of activities for some time. Though they are from the same geographical area, I think they are a good representation of all activity directors. Let's let them speak for themselves about their vocation and what it means to them.

Mary Blue, A.D., *Brethren Home,*
Flora, Indiana

"It's seeing the little accomplishments each day, the hugs you give, not the big things. It's saying, 'I understand how you feel.' It's discovering what each person is, where they are coming from. It's taking time to smell the roses," says Mary who has been an activity director for ten years.

Mary, like several other professional activity directors, says her position is not just a job, it's a ministry. "It's a good place to discover not only things about others but about yourself. You are constantly evaluating. Your attitude affects everyone. Being an activity director takes a very giving person, someone who likes variety, a patient person."

Mary's advice to other activity directors is: "Know your resources--that is become familiar with people and places who can assist you in performing your job better." She also encourages, all departments to learn to work together.

Millie McCarty, A.D., *Milner Community*
Health Care Center, Rossville, Indiana

Millie says, "It's not an eight-hour a day job. If they (residents) need me, I'm there. If one is sick, I am there. If one is in the hospital, I go to see him. If one dies, I go to the funeral home. For *every* one! This, to me, is a ministry. God showed me a long time ago I'd be doing this. This job is one of the most satisfying ones. I especially like one-on-one activities. I help them out of their depression. I come either down or up to their level. It's important, I feel, to read the residents' histories. You learn a lot about them."

Recently, Millie had a cold and was unable to visit a patient in the hospital, but she still phoned her and offered much encouragement. Another resident had not left his apartment for twelve years, from the time his wife died until he came to Millie's nursing home. She won him over. Later, when he was in the hospital and knew death was approaching, he called for Millie. Millie took two vacation days and spent the time at his bedside until he died. His last words were, "I wish I were your age so I could marry you." That is dedication. Most activity directors are unable to go to that length, yet Millie gives us an example of the deep relationships that often forms between residents and their activity director.

Millie tells that her four years as activity director have been quite different from working on the floor as an aide which she did for many years. "As an aide," she says, "you know the little physical things they like, but you don't really get to know them emotionally. As activity director, you enjoy knowing what makes them happy."

Sharon Heiser, A.D., *Indiana Pythian*
Home, Lafayette, Indiana

Sharon has worked in activities for eight years. "I sometimes feel like I have eighty kids," Sharon laughs. "My greatest satisfaction is when a resident says, 'Thank you, you made my day.' You learn to accept the little things as progress. An activity director must be willing to go beyond the call of duty. Being an activity director has made me appreciate my freedom--that I can eat when I want to eat, go home when I'm done or go out for an ice cream cone if I want one--a freedom residents don't have. Being an activity director lets me make my own schedule. If I've exhausted myself working with residents that day, I can work in my office or go shopping for supplies."

Janet Grubbs, A.D., *Americana Nursing Home, Lafayette, Indiana*

"It was a life-long goal of mine to be an activity director," says Janet. "I started as an aide. Before I was even an A.D., I used to hold spelling bees with them." Janet, too, feels that her job is a ministry. "It's a special gift," she says. "The secret of things running smoothly in a facility, I believe, is to win your staff over. Attitude goes around," she says. "If an activity director is cheerful, the patients will reflect her attitude, and when they are cheerful, the aides and nurses will be happier, too. When they are happy, the rest of the staff will be in better spirits. Residents look at me as a mother. Every month they want to vote for *me* as the employee-of-the-month. Just because they're old doesn't mean they can't laugh and have fun. Sometimes we're their only piece of sunshine. How can we be fun if we never use our smile?"

Janet's advice to new activity directors is: "Don't be in a hurry to change things. You'll upset everything. Allow them to think *they* are the ones changing things." She also says, "Remember you can't make everybody happy every time," and finally, "Love your job, enjoy your residents and get to really know the staff." She even offers an incentive to aides so they'll help bring residents to activities. "If you want a donut or whatever treat that residents are enjoying," she tells them, "bring two or three residents to activities." Janet says, "to be an activity director, it takes a certain type of person--not a Pollyanna. Other departments care for their (residents') bodies; you care for who they are--the spirit, the emotions, the feelings. You give encouragement and hope."

Dorothy Johnson, S.S., *Woodland Manor,*
Attica, Indiana

Dorothy has spent twelve years in activities, but now, nearing retirement, has switched to social service. "The job is always a challenge," says Dorothy. "Filling a human need is the most gratifying. I always try to find ways to give meaning to their life, yet it's a two-way street. You may help them, but they're really helping you. I've become a much better person since I've been here. You learn so much from your residents, wisdom and humility. You watch them, and they are so courageous and gallant in their sufferings. Then, when life gives you a bump on the head, you think of your residents and their suffering and that teaches you humility."

Dorothy feels it's very important to get her residents out into the community. She once involved them in a church Bible study program and let them give speeches to the church about life in the nursing home.

Asked how she has kept from burning out all these years, Dorothy was shocked at the word. "Well! Because I care about them. They're like family. I get so wrapped up in their lives."

To new activity directors, her advice is: "Don't get discouraged when others think your job is an easy one. There's so much detail that you take care of that others aren't aware of."

Rosemary Sherwood, A.D., *Westminster Village*
Health Center, West Lafayette, Indiana

Rosemary Sherwood has been an activity director for ten years. "It's satisfying to me to know how important we are to them. Just think where they would be without us." Rosemary speaks not boastfully, but out of sincere concern for her residents. "We must fulfill our obligation of improving the quality of life for them."

Michele Keller, A.D., *Otterbein Care Center*
Otterbein, Indiana

"You have to leave your problems at home," says Michele who's been an activity director for almost four years. "Two years can be the turning point in an A.D.'s career," she says,"determining whether you've got what it takes to be a professional activity director or not. You get satisfaction from your job. Caring for residents is satisfying. You feel like you're doing something worthwhile. It's like being a mom, you keep them entertained, you do things for them, and you help them with their homework."

Vicki Nichols, A.D., *Autumn Care Center,*
Ladoga, Indiana

Vicki has an been activity director for many years. She feels the greatest satisfaction of her job is getting to know so many people, especially her residents as they touch her life. "They share much with the A.D. They take me into their confidence," she says. Vicki's advice to fight burnout is to periodically change your programming. Also, she feels it's vital to have all the education in your field that you can get. "Education is needed on how to really listen," she says. "We must know our job, enjoy our residents and get to know ourselves. The staff can make or break an activity director. Our shoes are hard shoes to fill."

Barbara Houze, A.D., *Comfort Retirement*
and Nursing Home, Lafayette, Indiana

Barbara has been in activities for six years having worked for three facilities. "There's always a need. It's a constant challenge to be in activities. I never get bored. The residents are all different." Barbara, who is trained in music, involves it much in her program. "Music is the most wonderful therapeutic tool. Every resident in some way can respond to music. It reaches people." When stress levels are high--hers or residents'--she finds singing a welcome relief. Her advice to new activity directors is: "Be flexible. Everything is not cut and dried. Be open to new ideas, be open to residents who have contributed so much." Barbara also encourages activity directors to join activity director's groups for support.

Judie Kinnersley, A.D., S.S., *St. Elizabeth Hospital Extended Care Facility, Lafayette, Indiana*

Judie has been an activity director for many years and currently does both activities and social service. "It's satisfying to be there for other people. So often the activity director is not a threat to residents like those in uniform on staff can be. They open up to us." Judie feels a professional activity director is one who can really motivate and keep residents involved, one who can be there for them when they need her. Her advice to new activity directors is to become involved by joining organizations and keeping in close contact with other activity directors for support. Judie also advises A.D.'s to be careful of burnout. "Use volunteers to take some of the load off your shoulders."

Betty Goodman, A.D., *Green Hill Manor, Fowler, Indiana*

Betty Goodman has been an activity director about eleven years. Betty likes the personal contact with her residents. She says, "It's our job to help them overcome some of their handicaps through activities. We can pick up on their needs, find their values, pick up on old hobbies and get them involved again. We do so many small things that build up to a relationship. Residents learn to count on you."

Betty says what many activity directors are saying: "Residents in long-term care facilities seem to be sicker than they used to be, resulting in less participation at group activities. If they can't do activities, I'm there for them. I visit every patient every day. If they can't do anything, I have the communication for them." Betty loves people and appreciates when they do a good job. She says, "Sometimes I call certain aides into my office, and I say to them, 'You are a lovely person, so kind to these people.' I believe they need to be told their work and kindnesses are appreciated." Her advise to other A.D.'s is: "Stick with it. Tomorrow will bring new things. Sometimes you have to make things happen." Asked how she has managed to stick with her job and not burn out, Betty replies,"I love people, I guess."

Summary

There you have eleven professional activity directors. Each of them, like you, take their job very seriously. They put their residents interests first and know who they are and how important their position is, not only to the residents but to the facility in general. They are the bright spot in their residents' lives. Nurses push pills residents don't want; housekeeping move their belongings around; and dietary encourage them to eat when they are not hungry. You, the activity director, on the other hand, are their friend. You are their confidant--the one who sees to it that they are not bored, the one who cares when they are sad, and the one who rejoices with them when they are happy. You are there to challenge them, to encourage them and to continually provide creative new activities for them. You are there to enjoy their families with them, to hold their hand when they are sick, and often, to be at their side when they pass on to the next life.

Being an activity director is not an easy profession as so many think. You will certainly have days when you wish you were involved in any other occupation. But for a professional activity director--thank goodness--those days are few and far between. As you persevere in the field, you will undoubtedly increase in wisdom and insight. Compassion and love will continue to grow within your heart. You'll find yourself with a deeper understanding of life in general and a greater appreciation of it.

Yes, they are big shoes to fill. Professional activity directing requires a very special person--a gifted person, a unique person--and that person is **YOU**.

Congratulations!
YOU are a professional activity director!.

The End

Extras for You

Afterword

What the Future Holds For Activity Directors

By Bill Senteney

The profession of activity directing has only one way to go-- *UP!* That is if you are serious about your job and want to grow with it. Some will fall by the wayside when they find the challenge too great, but for those of you who prepare, there's a bright new future in your field.

Right now only five-percent of the elderly live in long-term care facilities, yet there is one out of nineteen elderly in need of some sort of care or service. This is the market of the future for those caring for the aged. Today we think 300 is a large facility, but when these elderly combine their assets and group together in community-type housing, a facility where they live might easily number 1000.

Few elderly desire to go to a nursing home. They feel that it *warehouses* them . They want to be as independent as possible yet it's difficult, both financially and physically, for them to remain in their own homes. Private enterprise more so than government will meet their need. They will provide large complexes where with residents' combined incomes, they can live jointly, somewhat like we see in Florida retirement centers today. These senior citizens will not be merely purchasing housing, but services as well--things they are either unable or unwilling to do--household up-keep, shoveling snow and mowing grass. In addition, they will demand a first-rate program of recreation to provide diversion in their many leisure hours. And that's where you come in!

Alert residents at these huge facilities will not be content with solely bingo and Bible studies for recreation, so the activity director will find herself in an entirely new role. She'll be what I call a *super-activity coordinator.* She will hold an executive position and will be a trained professional who understands elderly diversion. She will oversee a staff of activity specialists. She'll be planning trips to Jamaica as well as hiring and directing her staff to oversee the facility's golf course and the facility's riding stables. She will be better trained in supervision and will set precise goals, not just for residents, but for her staff as well. A major part of her position will be dealing in public relations, keeping her facility's name positively before the public.

Some activity directors will not be able to handle the challenge of this new dimension, but for those who can, now is the time to prepare. You will need a knowledge of computers because that is how scheduling will be done. You will need to understand subordinate motivation and learn all you can about supervision. You should begin now, if you haven't already, to integrate public relations into your activity program. At first, a college degree will probably not be required if you are already in activities.

So, if you are an activity director, you have many good things to look forward to in your future. Continue to take your job seriously, and grow with your field. That's what professional activity directing is all about.

Bill Senteney is president of his own company, "Independent Management." He began in the health care field as an administrator in 1965, coming up with Medicare and Medicaid. Today Bill speaks to groups all over the country and helps to teach the Indiana Health Care Association's course for administrators at Ball State University in Muncie. He has much wisdom which he generously shares and is an inspiration to activity directors who hear him speak.

Twenty Guidelines for the Professional Activity Director

1) A professional activity director dresses professionally. Dresses, suits or dress slacks with blazers present a professional image. An attractive hair style and personal neatness are important.

2) A professional activity director acts in a professional manner. She cannot afford to take part in facility gossip.

3) A professional activity director is organized both in her professional and her personal life. She plans her time wisely and carefully organizes her supplies. She keeps good records and can retrieve documents and supplies quickly when needed.

4) A professional activity director truly cares for her residents. She goes beyond the call of duty to meet their emotional needs. She finds herself acting as a liaison between residents and other staff; between residents and families.

5) A professional activity director has an active and varied program that seeks to meet the physical, mental, emotional and spiritual needs of residents. She constantly seeks ideas and is not afraid to try different activities. She regularly evaluates her program and does not allow it to become routine.

6) A professional activity director involves families closely in her program by holding resident/family activities several times a year.

7) A professional activity director involves her community in her activity program by offering services to them and by involving them closely with residents.

8) A professional activity director seeks to promote positively through the media, her facility's name. She learns to quickly spot a feature story in her activities or in her residents. She knows how to write a workable press release that will bring the media into her facility and bring forth good coverage.

9) A professional activity director, if she is in charge of the newsletter, does all in her power to perfect it and to use it as a public relations tool.

10) A professional activity director has a ready supply of word games and other back-ups for when her regularly scheduled activities fall through.

11) A professional activity director builds her a staff of volunteers, utilizes them fully, manages them wisely, appreciates them much and rewards them frequently.

12) A professional activity director gets her residents out of the facility and into the community at regular intervals.

13) A professional activity director becomes involved in professional activity director associations and does not hesitate to call another A.D. when she needs support.

14) A professional activity director develops a good working relationship with her administrator and other department heads. She learns to give when necessary and to stand her ground when necessary.

15) A professional activity director is always alert for signs of burnout. She is quick to take action to fight against it before it overtakes her.

16) A professional activity director recognizes herself for the professional she is and understands the importance of her position to the overall good of the facility.

17) A professional activity director learns to be assertive though not aggressive. She is able to ask for what she needs and desires for her department. She is also able, without fear of reprimand, to confidently bargain for better hours, and if she has earned them, higher wages.

18) A professional activity director puts others needs before her own, is aware of her own limitations and keeps a sense of humor when things go wrong.

19) A professional activity director is compassionate, trustworthy, adaptable and cheerful.

20) A professional activity director sets goals, both professional and personal, and seeks to meet them as she continues to grow as an activity director and as an individual.

Resources for Activity Directors

AARP
Program Scheduling Office
1909 K Street NW
Washington, DC 20049
(free-loan slide programs)

Activity Director's Guide
Eymann Publications, Inc.
1490 Huntington Circle, Box 3577
Reno, NV 89505
(newletter of activity ideas)

Briggs Activity Products
P.O. Box 1698
Des Moines, IA 50306
1-800-247-2343
(books, games, calendars, forms)

S & S. Worldwide
P.O. Box 517
Colchester, CT 06415-0517
1-800-243-9232
(books, games, crafts)

Dover Publications
31 E. 2nd St.
Mineola NY 11501
*(clip-art books, craft books,
historic paper dolls)*

Gold Timers
111 Center Ave., Suite 1
Pacheco, CA 94553
(510) 682-2428
(books and games)

Golden Horizons
R.R. 3 Box 364
Sullivan, IL 61951
(217) 728-8182
(books, balloons, trivia)

Medical Sales
2869 Bonderson
P.O. Box 1247
Omaha, NE 68112
402-457-3500
(books, games, etc.)

Modern Talking Pictures
500 Park St. N.
St. Petersburg, Fl 33709-9989
(free loan 16mm movies)

Nasco Activity Therapy
901 Janesville Ave.
Fort Atkinson, WI 53538
1-800-558-9595
*(books, games, art, and
party supplies)*

Basketball, Nursing Home Style

- Any number can play.
- Use a large rubber playground ball and a large reinforced cardboard bucket (like industrial soap comes in) or a weighted basket *(see photo in back of book)*.
- The game is played with everyone sitting down.
- Arrange residents in chairs and wheelchairs to form a circle.
- Make a real or imaginary line across the center of the circle.
- This line determines the two teams. Teams can have uneven numbers.
- On this line, in the center of the circle, set your bucket basket.
- Scoot chairs so residents are all approximately the same distance from the basket, three to seven feet, though if there are strong shooters, your circle might be more egg-shaped with the better shooters on the long ends.
- Someone will need to stand in the center of the circle next to the basket to retrieve the ball after each throw, and to hand it to the next player.
- It's very helpful to have someone, besides the one who acts as retriever for the ball, to keep score. Use a blackboard for this.
- The game begins as one team shoots for the basket. If he makes the basket, the ball goes to the other team to shoot. He receives one point. If he misses his shot, but the ball does *not* cross the imaginary center line, his team can shoot again, though the ball is passed to the player sitting next to the first shooter. If he misses and it doesn't cross the line again, it goes to the next player on his team. If he shoots and misses, but it crosses the center line, the opposite team gets to shoot in the same manner.
- The first team to 21 points is the winner.
- Give your team a name. Sports shops will sometimes donate T-shirts to sponsor your team. Put big numbers on the *front* of them.
- Teach the game to other facilities, and schools classes--kindergarten through college.
- Play a monthly game, either at your facility or at your opponent's. For an *away* game, you may want to take only about six players. For home games, many can play.
- Practicing once a week keeps their skills up and is exercise.
- When you get your team going, be sure to call the press.

(This activity warranted our facility a three-page spread in the Sunday magazine section of the newspaper, and later when we played Purdue, a front-page story.)

This game was developed by the author in 1980.

Medical Abbreviations

1) ASHD - arteriosclerotic heart disease
2) CBS - chronic brain syndrome
3) CHF - congestive heart failure
4) CVA - cerebrovascular accident
5) GI - gastrointestinal
6) GU - genitourinary
7) MI - myocardial infarction
8) OBS - organic brain syndrome
9) TIA - transient ischemic attack
10) CVD - cardiovascular disease
11) ac - before meals
12) pc - after meals
13) bid - twice a day
14) tid - three times a day
15) qid - four times a day
16) A.D.A.- American Diabetic Association
17) ↓ - Low Sodium
18) O_2 - oxygen
19) H_2O - water
20) prn - as needed
21) stat. - immediately
22) q - every
23) $\overline{c}$ - with
24) $\overline{s}$ - without
25) h - hour
26) NWB - non weight bearing
27) NPO - nothing by mouth
28) pt - patient
29) T.L.C. tender loving care
30) P.T. physical therapy

More Medical Terms and Abbreviations

1) a - without; an - without
2) ab - from, turn away; deviating
3) abdomin/o - abdomen
4) ad - toward - movement toward
5) adem/o - refers to glands
6) algea/i - overly sensitive to pain
7) amb/i - both
8) angi/o - vessel
9) anti - against
10) arteri/o - about the arteries
11) arthr/o - joints and bones
12) aut/o - self
13) bi - two
14) bio - life
15) brad/y - slow
16) carcin/o - cancerous tumor
17) cardi/o - about the heart
18) cephal/o - head
19) cerebr/o - brain
20) chlor/o - green
21) chol/o - gall - bile
22) col/o - col/ic - pertaining to colon
23) con - with
24) contra - against
25) crani/o - skull
26) cyan/o - blue, blueness
27) cyst/o - root word for bladder
28) cyt/o - cells
29) de - from
30) derm/o - referring to the skin
31) dermat/o - skin
32) cele - suffix - herniation
33) centesis - puncture or tapping
34) dis - to free, to undo

35) duoden/o - first part of small
36) dys - painful, bad, difficult
37) ectomy - removal
38) edema - fluid collection in tissue
39) emisis - vomiting
40) emia - refers to blood
41) epi - over
42) erythro/o - red
43) esthesia - feeling or sensation
44) eu - well or easy
45) ex - out from
46) extra - outside of or beyond
47) fibr/o - tumor containing fibers
48) gastr/o - stomach
49) gloss - tongue
50) glyc - sugar, glucose
51) gynec/o - woman
52) hemo - blood
53) hemi - half
54) hepat/o - pertaining to liver
55) hydro - water
56) hyper - above or more than
57) hypo - under or less
58) hyster/o - uterus
59) in - in or out
60) is/o - equal
61) itis - inflammation
62) kinesi/o - movement or motion
63) later/al - side
64) leps/y - seizures
65) leuk/o - white
66) lip/o - fat
67) lith/o - calculus or stone
68) lysis - destruction of tissue

69) macro - large
70) mal - poor or bad
71) mania - madness
72) medi/o - middle
73) micro/o - small
74) multi/i - many or more than one
75) my/o - muscles
76) narc/o sleep
77) nas/o - nose
78) necr/o -death
79) ne/o - new
80) nephr/o - refer to kidney
81) neur/o - nerve
82) noct/i - night
83) oid - resembles, like
84) oma - suffix for tumor
85) ophthalm/o - pertaining to eye
86) opia - vision
87) arrhagia - bursting forth of blood
88) arrhea - discharge
89) osis - condition
90) oste/o - bone
91) ostomy - forming a new opening
92) oto/o - ear
93) otomy - incision
94) para/a - near, beside, beyond
95) paralysis - loss of movement
96) path/o - disease
97) penia - decrease in
98) peps/o - digestion
99) per - through
100) peri - around
101) mono/o - one
102) phas/o - speech
103) phleb/o - vein
104) phono/o - voice or sound

105) pleur/o - refers to lung
106) pneu/o - breathe
107) pod/o - foot
108) pol/y - large
109) post - after
110) pre - before
111) pro - predicted
112) ptosis - prolapse or sag
113) pyel/o - renal pelvis (kidneys)
114) pyr/o -heat or fever
115) rect/o - pertaining to rectum
116) ren/o) - kidney
117) rhin/o - nose
118) scler/o - hardening
119) phag/o - eating/swallowing
120) stasis - stopping or controlling
121) sub - under, below
122) tack/y - fast, rapid
123) therap/o - treatment
124) therm/o - treatment
125) semi - half
126) sept/o - sepsis infection
       (poison state)
127) thromb/o - clot
128) tome - cutting out or into
129) trans - across or over
130) tri - three
131) troph/y - development
132) uni - one
133) vas/o - vessel
134) viscer/o - internal organs

Other Books By Marge Knoth

(current prices subject to change)
(shipping charges $4.00)

Newsletters Simplified! *This popular book is one of a kind!* *You'll find* 352 jammed-packed pages to help you turn out quickly, a lively newsletter that will be read cover to cover. Filled with information to put **IN** your newsletter. There's reminiscent articles, historical facts to write your own articles, funny stories, presidential and other trivia, one-liners, quotes, interesting statistics, comforting scriptures, old-time prices funny stories told by residents, and more. We've done the research for you! Also, five chapters on writing, proofing, designing and marketing. *Professionally printed, perfect-bound, 352 pages, **$19.99**. plus shipping.*

Activity Planning at Your Fingertips *A national award winner!* Offers over 600 activities with complete directions for each. Uniquely designed with 10 tabs for easy use, and then activities are listed alphabetically. Ideas for holiday parties, family parties, cooking, crafts, community outreaches, special projects, outings, men only, bedside and low-functioning, exercise, Christmas, clubs, monthly biggies, games, and more. Also, three-full years of pre-planned, pre-decorated activity calendars which you are free to copy and use. Has won state and national awards for its thorough contents and its user-friendly layout. A mini-library in itself. *208 pages, professionally wiro-bound, soft 3-color cover.* ***$26.99*** *plus shipping*

Remembering The Good Old Days *Residents will love this one!* All you need to lead a lively reminiscence group with no prior planning. Offers 100 old-days subjects, each broken down into a series of questions to ask residents (see chapter eight for sampling of format). Lots of old-time illustrations and pictures. *132 pages, perfect-bound **$13.99** plus shipping.*

Looking Back *Great when planned activity falls through!* Offers 200 challenging reminiscent questions and answers about life from 1890 to 1945. Great anytime you need a quick activity. Many illustrations. Sample questions: Why did early movies never show close-ups of people? *(They thought viewer would feel cheated seeing only half a person.)* What were mother-hubbard dresses? *(maternity clothes)* perfect-bound, 85-pages, **$10.99** plus shipping.

Master Planning Sheet

Daily	Weekly	Monthly	Yearly	Occasionally	Seasonally	New Ideas
		Projects	Community Involvement	Fill-ins	Outings	Cooking

Valley Press, P.O. Box 5224, Lafayette, IN 47903

Copyright © 1991 by Marge Knoth

Baby Contest

Making Sock Dolls

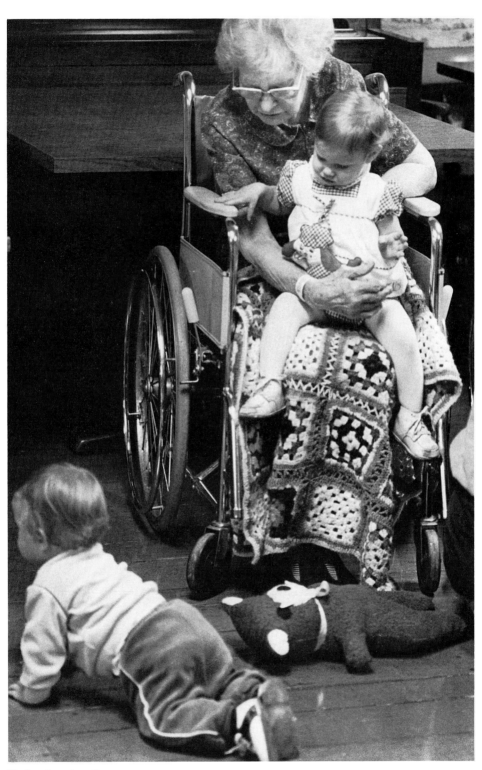

Baby Loving Day

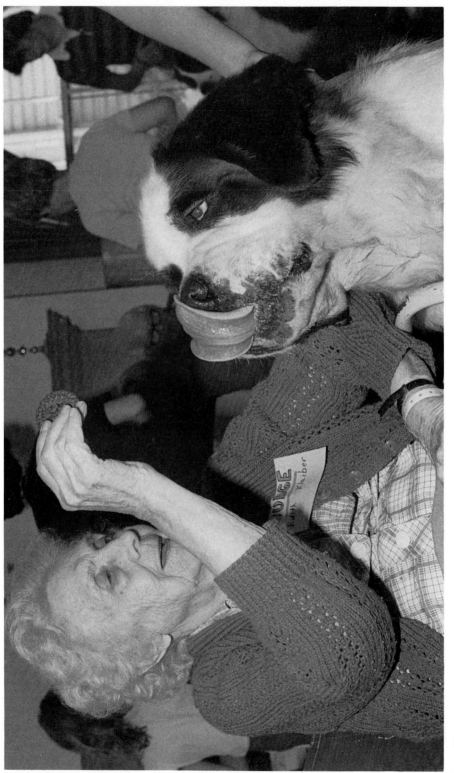

Pet Show

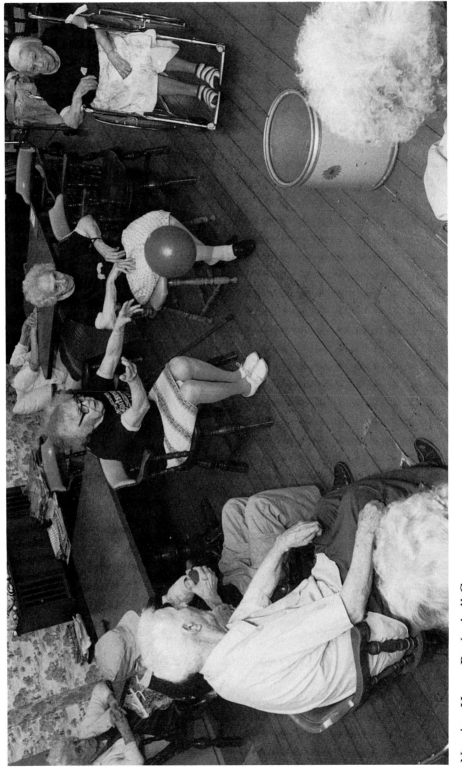

Nursing Home Basketball Game

Parade Downtown

Bowling with the Brownies

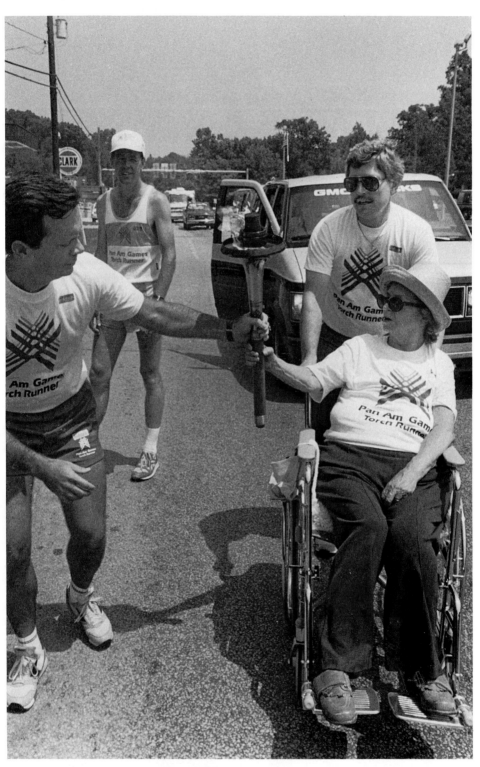

Pan American Games Torch Carrier